THE ONE BIG BOOK

GRADE 4

For English, Math, and Science

★ Includes Math, English, Science - all in one colorful book

★ Detailed instructions to teach and learn with pictures and examples

★ Best book for home schooling, practicing, and teaching

★ Includes answers with detailed explanations

Detailed instructions along with interesting activities

www.aceacademicpublishing.com

Author: Ace Academic Publishing

Prepaze is a sister company of Ace Academic Publishing. Intrigued by the unending possibilities of the internet and its role in education, Prepaze was created to spread the knowledge and learning across all corners of the world through an online platform. We equip ourselves with state-of-the-art technologies so that knowledge reaches the students through the quickest and the most effective channels.

The materials for our books are written by award winning teachers with several years of teaching experience. All our books are aligned with the state standards and are widely used by many schools throughout the country.

For enquiries and bulk order, contact us at the following address:

3736, Fallon Road, #403
Dublin, CA 94568
www.aceacademicpublishing.com

Ace Academic Publishing
ACHIEVING EXCELLENCE TOGETHER

ISBN: 978-1-949383-38-6

Other books from Ace Academic Publishing

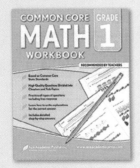 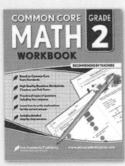  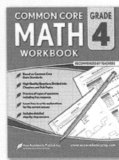 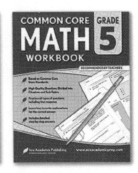

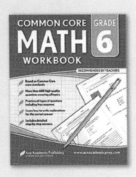 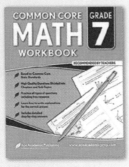 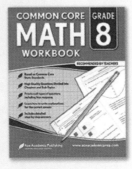  

Ace Academic Publishing

ACHIEVING EXCELLENCE TOGETHER

Other books from Ace Academic Publishing

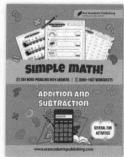

Contents

English

prepaze

Math

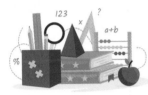

Science

prepaze

English

This book enables your children to explore the English language and develop the necessary expertise. A series of thought-provoking exercises, engaging activities, and engrossing puzzles facilitate your children with understanding the intricacies of the English language.

Language

Relative pronoun is a pronoun that introduces a relative clause. Who, whom, whose, which, and that are relative pronouns.

Examples

My grandpa, **who is 80**, has written many songs.

This is the car **that I received for graduation**.

In these examples, "who" and "that" are relative pronouns, and the underlined parts of the sentences are the relative clauses.

Relative adverb is an adverb that introduces a relative clause. Where, when, why, whenever, and wherever are relative adverbs.

Examples

It was raining **when we were in the mall**.

I don't know **why we have to stay here**.

In these examples, "when" and "why" are relative adverbs as they describe when something happened or why something happened. The underlined parts are the relative clauses.

complete Me!

Choose the best relative pronoun to complete each sentence.

1. This is the game _____ we should install.

   a) who

   b) that

   c) whose

2. The counselor with _____ I met was able to guide me.

   a) who

   b) whose

   c) whom

3. This is the ranch _____ we spent our vacation.

   a) that

   b) where

   c) which

4. The landlord _____ car is parked here is a nice person.

   a) which

   b) who

   c) whose

5. The woman _____ performed tonight is a teacher.

   a) who

   b) which

   c) whom

6. Dad bought the book, _____ was on sale.

a) where

b) which

c) whose

Word Puzzle

Find the relative pronouns and adverbs.

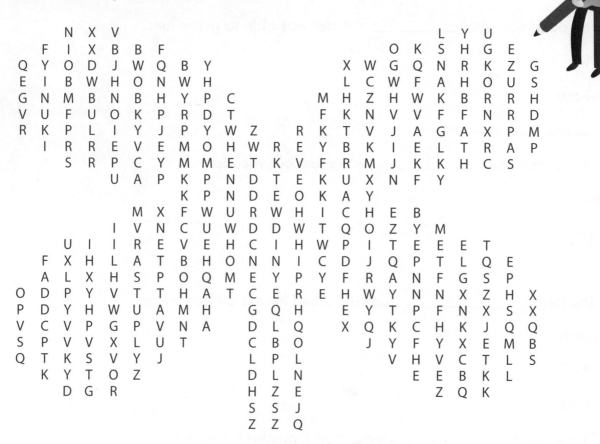

WHERE	WHY	WHOM	WHICH	WHOMEVER
WHEN	WHO	THAT	WHOEVER	WHICHEVER

Progressive Verb Tense

The progressive tense is used to show an action that is ongoing in some point in time. There are three progressive tenses: present progressive, past progressive, and future progressive.

Examples

They **were rehearsing** for a play. (past progressive)

They **are rehearsing** for a play. (present progressive)

They **will be rehearsing** for a play. (future progressive)

prepaze

Change the Tense

Transform the sentences from present or future progressive to past progressive.

Example

She is waiting for her mom.

She **was waiting** for her mom.

1. I am walking in the park.
_____

2. They will be helping others.
_____

3. Where are you going?
_____

4. They are studying.
_____

5. He will be looking at the photos.
_____

6. She will be painting.
_____

7. Jack is being nice.
_____

8. I will be reading.
_____

Which one Is It?

Find the tense of the sentences and shade the stars against the right answers.

1. My brother is working today.

☆ past progressive

☆ present progressive

☆ future progressive

2. She was chasing the dog.

☆ past progressive

☆ present progressive

☆ future progressive

3. The children are swimming in the pond.

☆ past progressive

☆ present progressive

☆ future progressive

4. I will be visiting her today.

☆ past progressive

☆ present progressive

☆ future progressive

5. It is raining.

☆ past progressive

☆ present progressive

☆ future progressive

6. The shop will be closing soon.

☆ past progressive

☆ present progressive

☆ future progressive

prepaze

Modal Auxiliaries

Modal auxiliary verbs are used to indicate ability, possibility, permission, or intention. The following are modal verbs: can, could, may, might, shall, should, will, would, and must. Unlike other verbs, these verbs do not have different forms such as "-ing" to show progressive tense, or "-s" to form singular verbs.

Examples

Could I open the door, please? (permission)

We **might** go to Italy next year. (possibility)

Crossword Puzzle

Use the clues to find the modal auxiliary verbs such as could, may, or can to complete the puzzle.

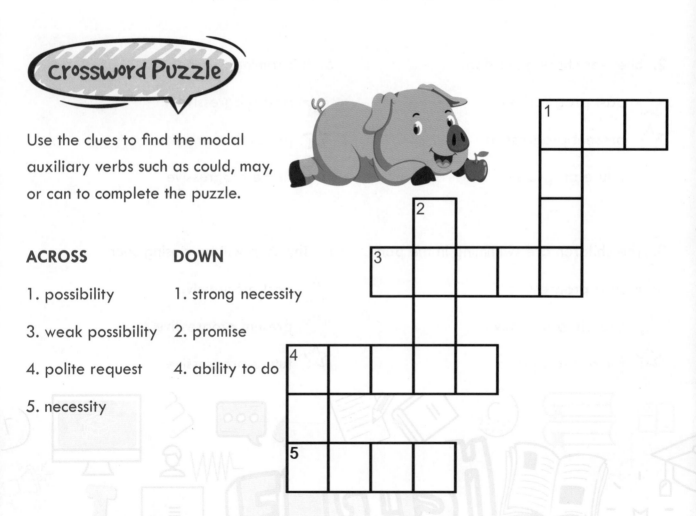

ACROSS

1. possibility

3. weak possibility

4. polite request

5. necessity

DOWN

1. strong necessity

2. promise

4. ability to do

Missing Verbs

Complete the sentences using the appropriate verbs from the parentheses.

1. _____ I come in? [Can, May]

2. These things _____ to be done. [need, must]

3. _____ you mind if I join you? [Could, Would]

4. He is sick. He _____ stay home. [must, can]

5. She says she _____ do it. [need, will]

order of Adjectives

An adjective is used to describe or give more information about a noun.

Example

small house

The word small tells us the size of the house.

More than one adjective can be used to describe the house.

Example: a spooky small blue house

When we use more than one adjective to describe a person, place, or thing, we have to follow an order. The following is the order in which adjectives should be used.

determiner	opinion	size	shape	age	color	origin	material	purpose	noun

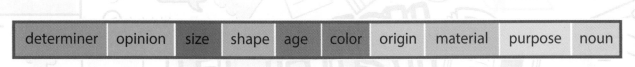

Jumbled Sentences

Rearrange the adjectives in the correct order.

1. We bought **blue new a** van.

2. I see **red a plastic big** box.

3. Mom uses **Italian old an** pasta recipe.

4. She gave **round little cute a** bowl.

5. It is **a black metal beautiful** lamp.

Picture in Words

Write two sentences describing the pictures. Write the third sentence combining the descriptive words.

Example:

We won **a gold** trophy.

We won **a shiny** trophy.

We won **a shiny gold** trophy.

1.

_____

_____

_____

2.

_____

_____

_____

3.

4.

Prepositional Phrases

A prepositional phrase includes a preposition followed by its object. Sometimes a modifier is included in a prepositional phrase.

Examples

We are **in the car.**

Here "in" is the preposition and "the car" is the object of the preposition.

We are **in my cousin's car.**

Here "in" is the preposition and " car" is the object of the preposition, and "my cousin" is the modifier.

Complete Me!

Using the prepositions given in the box complete the prepositional phrases.

into	over	outside	from	on

1. Mom said, "Play _____ the house."

2. Jane has travelled all _____ the world.

3. Water was leaking _____ the ceiling.

4. The lion ran _____ the forest.

5. I got many gifts _____ my birthday.

Make Sentences

Write 4 sentences using prepositional phrases.

1. _____

2. _____

3. _____

4. _____

Fragments and Run-ons

What are fragments?

Fragments are incomplete sentences. Every sentence should convey a complete thought using a subject and a predicate.

Example

Fragment: Waiting for you.

(lacks a subject)

Revised: I'm waiting for you.

What are run-ons?

This happens when two or more independent clauses are joined without proper punctuation or conjunction. There are three common ways to fix a run-on sentence as shown in the below example.

Example

Run-on: He was late for the meeting he took a cab.
(lacks conjunction/punctuation)

Revised: He was late for the meeting, **so** he took a cab.
(comma + coordinating conjunction)

OR

Revised: He was late for the meeting; he took a cab. (semicolon)

OR

Revised: He was late for the meeting. **He** took a cab. (period)

prepaze

Match the Parts

Match the following to make complete sentences.

She is	I'll call you
They are	looking out the window
Bikes of all kinds	to explain why she did that
After I leave home	are in the shop
He wrote	gathered to welcome him

fragments, Run-ons, or No Error?

Identify the following as a fragment, run-on, or no error sentence.

1. As soon as we reached the airport.

   ☐ **fragment**

   ☐ **run-on**

   ☐ **no error**

2. Children were playing outside while it rained.

   ☐ **fragment**

   ☐ **run-on**

   ☐ **no error**

3. They wrapped the presents and they arranged them under the tree.

   ☐ **fragment**

   ☐ **run-on**

   ☐ **no error**

4. Larry who adopted the cat.

   ☐ **fragment**

   ☐ **run-on**

   ☐ **no error**

5. He often runs around a lot so his mother worries about him.

   ☐ **fragment**

   ☐ **run-on**

   ☐ **no error**

6. Although they created the designs before they got the project.

   ☐ **fragment**

   ☐ **run-on**

   ☐ **no error**

fix Me!

Complete the below fragments by adding the missing subject or predicate.

1. A project that was difficult to make.

   _____

2. When you are on the road.

   _____

3. Make up a story.

   _____

4. With the holidays around the corner.

   _____

5. Trying to convince me.

   _____

prepaze

Below are a few run-ons. Rewrite them by adding the necessary punctuation marks and conjunctions.

You can fix a run-on by

- adding a comma + conjunction

- adding a semicolon

- splitting the sentence into two using a period

Here's one done for you.

She was robbed she went to the police station.

, so (comma + conjunction "so")

She was robbed⌃she went to the police station.

1. It is sunny today we are going to the beach.

_____

2. You can meet the warden she will show you the room.

_____

3. It started to rain we continued playing outside.

_____

4. We usually read before bed sometimes our mom reads to us.

_____

5. It's gross I don't want to see it ever again in my life.

_____

prepaze

A few words in English that have the same spelling but different sound, or words that have the same sound but different spelling can be confusing when writing.

Examples

Word	Meaning	Used in Sentence
minute	60 seconds	We have 10 **minutes** more.
minute	tiny	That was a **minute** mistake.

Word	Meaning	Used in Sentence
to	motion toward a point	Have you been **to** Canada?
too	in addition/higher degree	You are driving **too** fast.
two	number	We met **two** years ago.

This or That?

Fill in the blanks with the commonly confused words

desert or dessert

1. Mom prepared a cake for _____ .

2. One-fifth of the Earth's land area is covered by _____ .

it's or its

3. The cat eats _____ food in that corner.

4. _____ not fair.

lose or loose

5. These clothes are _____ now.

6. Did our team _____ the game?

than or then

7. She is taller _____ him.

8. Back _____ , we worked in the same place.

prepaze

9. Is [   ] a coffee shop on this road?

10. They are happy with [   ] work.

11. [   ] proud of you.

Make Sentences

Write a sentence for the following confusing words.

1.
affect	
effect	

2.
led	
lead	

3.
than	
then	

4.
past	
passed	

5.
there	
their	

prepaze

Capitalizing the correct words will show the readers you know what you are doing. The following are the basic rules of capitalization.

- The first word of every sentence needs to be capitalized.

- The pronoun 'I' is always capitalized.

- The proper name of a person, place, or thing is always capitalized.

Examples

Evelyn and Jackson visit Yellowstone National Park every June.

Underline the words that need to be capitalized.

1. my favorite movie is the lion king.

2. violet and i are cousins.

3. next week, we have tests on math, english, and spanish.

4. my birthday is on 20th july.

5. we visited the statue of liberty on the thanksgiving day.

Punctuation

There are many punctuation marks in the English language. They provide clarity to our writing. Here are a few of them:

Commas are used in lists, to set apart a phrase or a clause, and in direct speech.

Exclamation marks are used after an interjection or exclamation.

Quotation marks are used when someone else's words need to be reported.

Semicolons are used to connect two independent clauses.

Examples

Jacob exclaimed, "It is unbelievable!"

The children enjoyed playing in the water at the beach; they, however, wanted to go to the theme park.

Rewrite the sentences by adding proper punctuation marks.

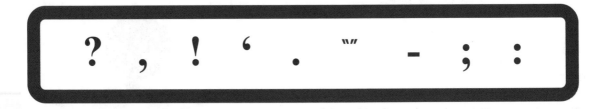

1. He said I won

_____

2. Who did that

_____

3. They are good funny and hardworking

_____

4. Oh dear She must be devastated

_____

5. She went to California last week she will return this weekend

Spelling

Do you find spelling challenging? You are not alone. Spelling can be tricky in English due to many factors. You can improve spelling by reading and writing as frequently as you can.

Examples

The following are a few factors that make spelling challenging:

• foriegn words/loanwords (faux pas)

• confusing words (stationary, stationery)

Unscramble the Words

Rearrange the letters to find the words.

1. | N | H | U | R | G | Y | → | | | | | | |

2. | W | I | T | S | C | H | → | | | | | | |

3. | L | P | R | I | A | → | | | | | |

4. | S | A | P | E | C | → | | | | | |

5. | G | A | E | R | D | → | | | | | |

6. | S | D | S | I | S | C | U | → | | | | | | | |

7. | T | H | M | Y | → | | | | |

8. | S | N | D | U | O | → | | | | | |

Spot the odd one

Color the misspelled words in green.

| theirs | coast | plaine | rural |

| teamate | genre | nowhere | worthy |

| laundry | hyperbol | laboratory | provide |

| furniture | continue | whistel | feedback |

| expression | agriculture | boundary | athelete |

| grammer | measure | kilometer | resistor |

prepaze

Multiple Meaning Words

In English, many words have more than one meaning. Such words are called multiple meaning words.

Example

BAT

Show the Difference!

Write a pair of sentences for the following multiple meaning words. In each pair, use a different meaning of the word. You can refer to a dictionary for help.

1.

bear

2.

light

3.

sink

4.

leaves

5.

coach

Crossword Puzzle

Find the multiple meaning words to complete the puzzle.

ACROSS

2. He dipped his toe in the _____ . The _____ table was occupied.

4. She is a _____ person. This is not that _____ of a show.

5. The box was about 3_____ tall. He tapped his _____ listening to the songs.

DOWN

1. It weighs 7 _____ . My heart _____ with excitement.

3. The dress is _____ as a feather. The _____ bulb glows.

Context Clues

Do you come across words for which you don't know the meaning? If so, don't panic.

The writers often leave clues to guess the meaning of unfamiliar words.

Example

Nick's speech was **immaculate**.

The above sentence has an unfamiliar word, but there aren't enough clues to guess the meaning.

Nick's speech was **immaculate** unlike Peter's messy speech.

In the above sentence, the context clarifies that immaculate is unlike (opposite of) "messy." With that, we can conclude that immaculate means clean and perfect.

Guess the Meaning!

Use the context clues to find the meaning of the underlined words.

1. I rode home with a **<u>loquacious</u>** cab driver. He kept talking all the way.

 a) humble

 b) good looking

 c) talkative

2. We were able to bring our laptops as the teacher **acceded** to our request.

a) forced

b) agreed

c) rejected

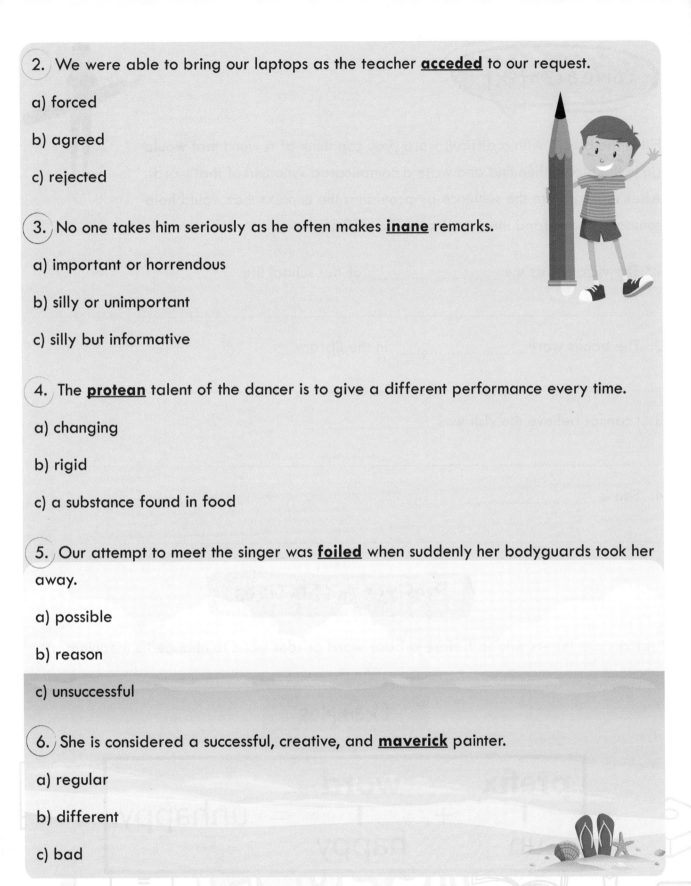

3. No one takes him seriously as he often makes **inane** remarks.

a) important or horrendous

b) silly or unimportant

c) silly but informative

4. The **protean** talent of the dancer is to give a different performance every time.

a) changing

b) rigid

c) a substance found in food

5. Our attempt to meet the singer was **foiled** when suddenly her bodyguards took her away.

a) possible

b) reason

c) unsuccessful

6. She is considered a successful, creative, and **maverick** painter.

a) regular

b) different

c) bad

Give a Context

Fill in the blanks with a difficult word (you can think of a word that would go in the blank, then find and write a complicated synonym of that word). After that, rewrite the sentence by providing the context that would help someone understand the meaning of the difficult word.

1. The victory was the _____ of her school life.

_____

2. The books were _____ in the library.

_____

3. I cannot believe the visit was _____ .

_____

4. She is _____ .

_____

Prefixes and Suffixes

Prefixes are letters added before a base word or root word to change its meaning or function.

Examples

prefix + **word** = unhappy
un   happy

Suffixes are letters added at the end of a base word or root word to change its meaning or function.

word + **suffix** = laughed
laugh + ed = laughed

This or That?

Color the words with prefixes in green , words with suffixes in yellow , and words with no affixes in blue .

react	school	neighborhood
beautiful	invisible	company
hard	week	enjoy
struggle	class	quietly

Match the words with prefixes

over	marine
a	phone
dis	cook
en	approve
mega	case
sub	moral

Match the words with suffixes

kind   ous

clock   ful

humor   ment

season   wise

move   ness

wonder   al

Reference Materials

We often hear people convey different ideas or opposite notions on something. We can use a reference material on such occasions to get a clear idea on a topic at hand. There are many reference materials readily accessible.

Examples

dictionary
encyclopedia
atlas
maps
directories

Word Chain

How to play:

- Look up the entry words in a dictionary.

- There may be more than one meaning for an entry word, pick any one and write it.

- From the meaning words, pick a word and write it in the next line as a new entry word.

- Look up the new entry word in the dictionary again. Write the meaning of the new entry word. From the meaning words, pick a word and write it in the next line as a new entry word.

- Ensure that the words you choose as entry words are more than 4 letters long.

- Repeat this 4 times for each word.

Example

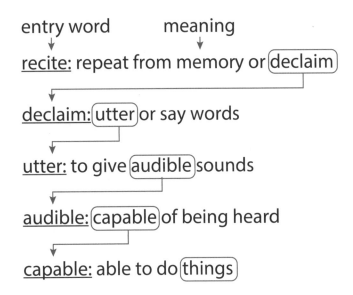

entry word   meaning

recite: repeat from memory or declaim

declaim: utter or say words

utter: to give audible sounds

audible: capable of being heard

capable: able to do things

Create a word chain for the words: process, abound, decline, and benevolent.

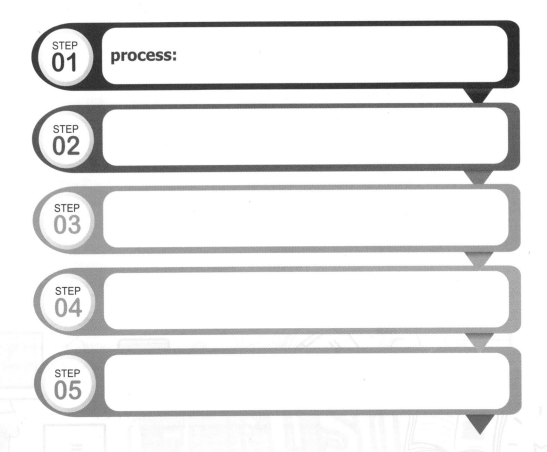

STEP 01   **process:**

STEP 02

STEP 03

STEP 04

STEP 05

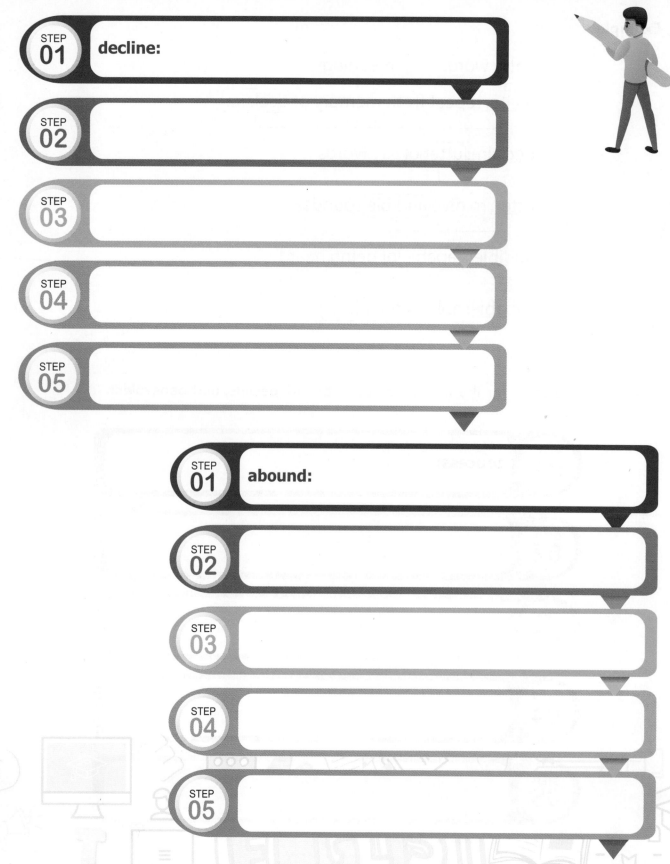

STEP 01 decline:

STEP 02

STEP 03

STEP 04

STEP 05

STEP 01 abound:

STEP 02

STEP 03

STEP 04

STEP 05

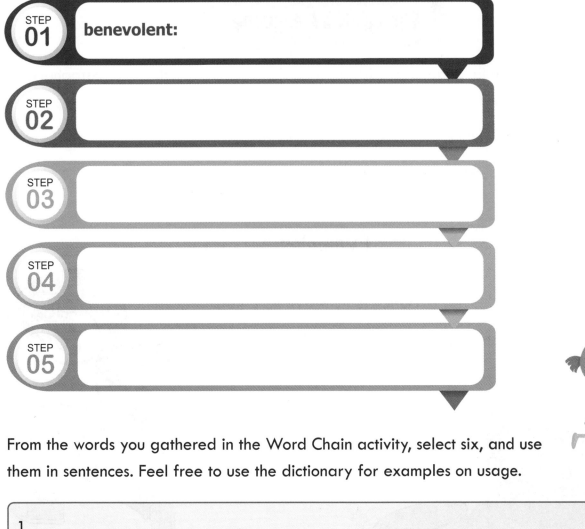

STEP 01 benevolent:

STEP 02

STEP 03

STEP 04

STEP 05

From the words you gathered in the Word Chain activity, select six, and use them in sentences. Feel free to use the dictionary for examples on usage.

1

2

3

4

5

6

Keep expanding your vocabulary and use the words in writing and speech.

Figurative Language

Writers use figurative languages to add depth to their writing. Similes and metaphors are examples of figurative language.

A **simile** compares two things using the words "like" or "as."

A **metaphor** compares two things without using the words "like" or "as."

Examples

Derick is as brave as a lion.

The simile here shows how **Derick** is brave as a **lion**.

Susan is a shining star.

The metaphor here directly compares Susan to a shiny star instead of using any specific attribute of a star.

This metaphor could mean that the person is bright or outstanding.

prepaze

Simile or Metaphor?

Label the following sentences as simile or metaphor and explain your answer.

Example: My closet is as tall as a giraffe.

label	explain
simile	the closet is directly compared to a giraffe

1. The morning outside was as cold as ice.

label	explain

2. Her smile lights up the room.

label	explain

3. I was hungry as a bear.

label	explain

4. The baby sleeps like a log.

label	explain

5. He is a night owl.

label	explain

Create Similes!

Write three similes comparing two things directly.

1.

2.

3.

Create Metaphors!

Write three metaphors with hidden comparison.

1.

2.

3.

prepaze

Antonyms

Antonyms mean opposite meanings of words. These words help us express ourselves better.

Example

BIG   **SMALL**

Circle the antonyms of the underlined words as used in the text.

1. After school, they always played <u>together</u>.

silently   separately   away

2. They were <u>inseparable</u>.

worried   close   unfriendly

3. When they went to the gym, Simon <u>joined</u> them.

left   partly   sent

4. The others were equally scared, but <u>excited</u> to see what it held.

thrilled   happy   bored

5. They <u>took</u> it to Anna's tree house.

left   lost   buried

6. The lion was <u>ferocious</u>, which scared off the children.

violent   nearby   gentle

Write the opposite meaning words for the following. You may use a dictionary for help!

1. length   X

2. neat   X

3. under   X

4. cheap   X

full

prepaze

5. borrow   X   [ ]

6. shallow   X   [ ]

empty

7. weak   X   [ ]

8. cruel   X   [ ]

Riddle

Look at the following words:

WOOLLEN

BALLOON

COOLLY

Do you find any similarity among these three words?

Each word has two double letters. Not only that, the double letters appear consecutively.

Your turn. Give a word with three consecutive double letters.

[ ]

Reading: Literature

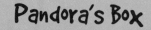

Pandora's Box

Becka, May, John, and Lance were friends. They lived in the same neighborhood. After school, they always played together in Becka's yard, in John's tree house, or in the streets. They were inseparable[1].

One day after school, Lance and John went to Becka's place. Soon after, May joined them. Becka told them, "In my yard, I saw a huge worm crawl into the ground this morning." All the friends jumped to their feet and said, "Let's find that worm."

They went to the yard with a shovel and spade[2]. Becka showed others where she saw the worm. Excited to catch the worm, the friends started digging.

After digging for a while, they felt exhausted[3], but did not find the worm. They continued to dig. They heard a clunk as Lance's shovel hit on something. They removed the dust over it and found a treasure chest.

prepaze

The chest looked old, black, dirty, and eerie[4]. May exclaimed[5], "Oh! This looks like a Pandora's box. We better not open it!" The others were equally scared, but excited to see what it held.

They took it to John's tree house where no one could find it, and decided not to open it ever. After two days, they went to the tree house and opened it anyway. As soon as they opened the box, the tree house shook fiercely, and they heard loud noises. As they looked at each other and the content of the chest in shock, May said, "We've definitely opened a Pandora's box!!"

---

[1] inseparable: people who spend more time together; [2] shovel and spade: tools used for digging; [3] exhausted: tired; [4] eerie: strange and scary; [5] exclaimed: talk loudly due to excitement or fear

Story Elements

1. What are the names of Becka's friends?

_____

2. Why did the friends decide to go to the yard?

_____

3. What does "the Pandora's box" mean according to May?

_____

4. Where did they hide the treasure chest?

_____

prepaze

order Me

Number the events in the order in which they happened in the story.

Found a treasure chest instead of the worm

Friends geared up to find the worm

Friends were in trouble

Hid the treasure chest

Becka saw a huge worm in her yard

Dug up the yard

Number the events in the order in which they happened in the story.

Unscramble the words from the passage

A	R	T	E	F

→ ▢ ▢ ▢ ▨ ▢

E	B	C	K	A

→ ▨ ▢ ▢ ▢ ▢

R	D	P	A	N	A	O

→ ▢ ▢ ▢ ▨ ▢ ▢

H	O	E	S	U

→ ▢ ▨ ▢ ▢

G	D	I

→ ▢ ▨ ▢

O	E	T	H	R

→ ▨ ▢ ▢ ▢ ▢

Unscramble the letters from the blue box to reveal the message

▨ ▨   ▨ ▨ ▨ ▨

Creative Writing

Are you eager to find out what happened next in "Pandora's Box"?
Imagine you were one of the four friends, and build the story further.
Feel free to add more characters, settings, and twists.

Bullying

Ben, Sasha, and I had been best friends since kindergarten. One day, we were on the last seat of the school bus excited to reach school and begin our first day of fifth grade. I noticed a new girl on the bus.

She was sitting quietly by herself. We all reached school and enjoyed the day. The new girl, Penny, looked shy and no one talked to her. Since Ben, Sasha, and I were close, we did not want to add her to our group.

Weeks passed and Penny struggled[1] to make new friends. The bigger children in the class bullied[2] her and made her cry sometimes. One day, we were asked to do a project. Her project looked beautiful, but before the teacher entered the class, it was broken by one of the children. We pitied her, but we did not react.

On the same day, I went to a party with my older brother. My brother was having fun with his friends while I was sitting alone in a corner. No one cared to talk to me. I felt invisible[3] and left out. This made me realize how hard it would be for Penny in classroom.

Next day, I sat beside her on the bus. Seeing me, Ben and Sasha also sat with us. We became friends instantly[4]. We kept her company on the bus, in the classroom, and in the cafeteria.

That was the first day I saw her smile. I felt good making someone happy, and no one bullied her since then.

[1] struggled: made great effort; [2] bullied: harassed, threatened, or harmed someone; [3] invisible: not seen or ignored; [4] instantly: at once

Story Analysis

1. *She was sitting quietly by herself.*

   Why was Penny quiet?

   _____

2. *Weeks passed and Penny struggled to make new friends.*

   Why do you think it was hard for Penny to make friends?

   _____

3. Why were other children bullying Penny?

   _____

4. When did the narrator realize it is horrible to be ignored by others?

   _____

Connecting to Text

1. Have you experienced bullying? What happened and when did it happen?

_____

_____

2. Give two examples of bullying.

_____

_____

_____

3. What would you do if a new girl or boy in your class struggles to make friends?

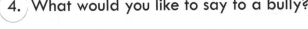

_____

_____

4. What would you like to say to a bully?

_____

_____

prepaze

New Brooms, Brooms, O!

There was an old man, and he lived in a wood;

And his lazy son Jack would snooze till noon:

Nor followed his trade although it was good,

With a bill and a stump for making of brooms, green brooms;

With a bill and a stump for making of brooms.

One morn[1] in a passion, and sore with vexation[2],

He swore he would fire the room,

If he did not get up and go to his work,

And fall to the cutting of brooms, green brooms, etc.

Then Jack he arose and slipt[3] on his clothes,

And away to the woods very soon,

Where he made up his pack, and put it on his back,

Crying, Maids, do you want any brooms? green brooms, etc.

- Joseph Ritson

[1] morn: morning; [2] vexation: being annoyed; [3] slipt: slipped

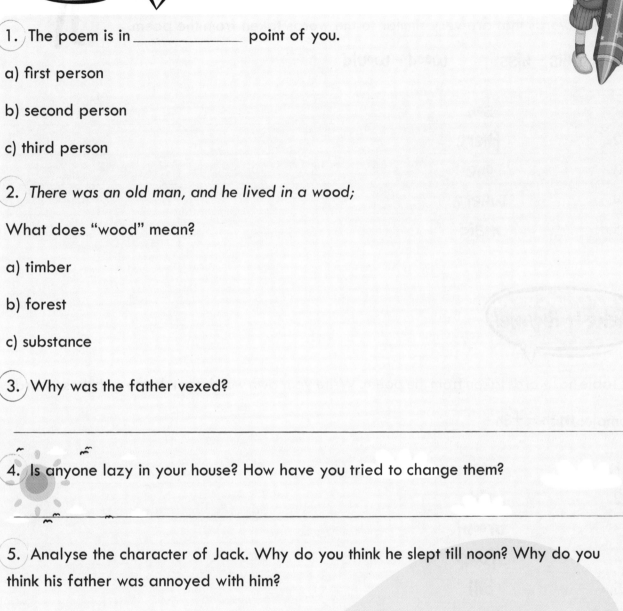

Poem Appreciation

1. The poem is in _____ point of you.

   a) first person

   b) second person

   c) third person

2. *There was an old man, and he lived in a wood;*

   What does "wood" mean?

   a) timber

   b) forest

   c) substance

3. Why was the father vexed?

   _____

4. Is anyone lazy in your house? How have you tried to change them?

   _____

5. Analyse the character of Jack. Why do you think he slept till noon? Why do you think his father was annoyed with him?

   _____

   _____

6. Write an example for cause and effect from the poem.

   _____

Write the words that are very similar to the words taken from the poem.

Examples his – hiss   wood – would

1.	son	
2.	there	
3.	one	
4.	where	
5.	maid	

This table has words taken from the poem. Write your own words that rhyme with these words.

Example: man – tan

1.	noon	
2.	old	
3.	broom	
4.	stump	
5.	bill	
6.	trade	
7.	sore	
8.	passion	
9.	work	
10.	green	

 **Let's Rap?**

Time to put on a rapper's hat! Here are a few tips for you.

 **Step 1**
Choose a theme such as: friendship, love, kindness, bravery. Or choose a theme of your own.

 **Step 2**
Write the rap with a rhythm and flow in a way that it can be rapped to your family members.

 **Step 3**
Throw in a few rhyming words or metaphor/simile to make it interesting.

 **Step 4**
Though a poem does not require proper punctuation or grammar, make sure you use a few capitalization and punctuation.

 **Step 5**
Proofread your work.

 **Step 6**
Show to others and get their feedback.

 **Step 7**
Be willing to make changes after feedback!

Step 8
Don't forget to sign off with your name.

·····································

·····································

·····································

·····································

·····································

·····································

·····································

·····································

·····································

by ·····································

Cinderella – A Fairy Tale

Once upon a time a girl named Cinderella lived with her stepmother and two stepsisters. The stepmother and sisters treated Cinderella cruelly and made her do all the work for them, yet Cinderella was kind and treated everyone equally.

One day, the king announced[1] a ball for his son. The stepsisters envied[2] Cinderella's beauty and ensured she would stay home while they went to the ball. The day of the ball arrived, and every girl in the kingdom went to the ball. When the stepsisters and stepmother left, a fairy godmother appeared and saw Cinderella crying.

The fairy wanted to help Cinderella to get to the ball. She turned a pumpkin into a carriage[3], turned the mice into horses, and lizard into a servant. She waved her wand and changed Cinderella's filthy clothes into a beautiful gown. The fairy sent Cinderella off to the palace telling her that all the magic will go away by midnight.

At the ball, Cinderella met the prince, and they fell in love. Moments before the clock struck 12, Cinderella ran away from the palace leaving behind a glass shoe, which the prince found. He sent his men to every house to make the girls try on that shoe.

The shoe fit Cinderella perfectly.

The prince married Cinderella, and they lived happily ever after.

[1] announced: to tell people about something; [2] envied: to wish you had something that others had; [3] carriage: a vehicle

1. What is the theme of the story?

a) greed as downfall

b) good wins over evil

c) love and sacrifice

2. Who are the antagonists (evil/bad characters) in the story?

a) stepmother

b) stepsisters

c) stepmother and stepsisters

3. Why did the fairy turn a pumpkin into a carriage?

a) to take Cinderella to the ball

b) to add as accessory for her clothes

c) to punish the pumpkin

4. Why was it important that Cinderella left the ball before midnight?

a) she will be caught by her stepsisters if she did not return home before them

b) the fairy godmother will disappear

c) the objects created by fairy's magic will return to normal

Story in Pictures

Describe each of the below pictures with two sentences of your own.

Scene 1

....

....

....

Scene 2

....

....

....

Scene 3

....

....

....

Scene 4

....

....

....

Scene 5

....

....

....

Scene 6

....

....

....

My Baby Sister

My name is Nash. I live with my parents and my baby sister Eva.

One day my mom took my baby sister and me to the park. While I played with my sister on the see-saw, my mom went for a walk around the park.

After that, Eva and I played on the slides for some time. Then, I went to play on the swing. Eva came running after me and climbed on my lap.

I was careful as Eva was on my lap. Eva was so excited that she said, "Let's go higher! Higher!" So, I swung fast and high. When we were high in the air, I felt her slipping away. Before I could hold her tight, she fell to the ground.

Eva scraped her knees and cried in pain. Mom saw Eva crying and came over. I told her what happened. She said, "It's okay, Nash. I know you did not do it on purpose[1]. Let's get her cleaned up."

Later, mom asked me to take good care of my sister while playing to avoid such accidents[3].

[1] purpose: the aim or intention of something

Story Analysis

1. Who are there in Nash's family?

_____

2. Where did Nash, his mom, and sister go?

_____

3. What did Nash and Eva do as soon as they reached the park?

_____

4. How did Eva scrape her knees?

_____

5. When did mom notice something was wrong?

_____

6. Who is narrating the story?

a) a narrator   b) Nash   c) Eva

7. What point of view is the story written in?

a) first person   b) second person   c) third person

8. Give an example for cause and effect from the story.

_____

prepaze

Character Analysis

1. What can be said about Nash? Circle the right answer and explain your answer in the line below.

a) honest and caring

b) liar and unreliable

c) happy and funny

_____

_____

_____

2. What can be said about the mom? Circle the right answer and explain your answer in the line below.

a) understanding and loving

b) rude and understanding

c) loving but unforgiving

_____

_____

_____

Match the sequence number with the events.

1	**played on the slide**
2	**scraped the knees**
3	**reached the park**
4	**went home**
5	**fell off the swing**

Poem vs. Prose

Jack a Nory

I'll tell you a story

About Jack a Nory;

And now my story's begun:

I'll tell you another

About Jack his brother

And now my story's done.

-Joseph Ritson

My Favorite Book

On my last birthday, my grandma gave me a book. I enjoyed reading it with her. Earlier this week, we boxed away things for charity and cleaned our house. After a couple of days when I wanted to read that book that my grandma gave, I realized it was missing.

My dad, grandma, and I looked all over the house. I looked for it in my closet, bag, shelves, and everywhere. My dad searched the entire house. Seeing me sad, my grandma grabbed the boxes set aside for charity.

She found the book and exclaimed, "Here it is!" I thanked my grandma and asked her to read it to me again!

Find the Difference

Circle the correct answer and then explain the reason on the right.

1. *Jack a Nory* is a   Why? Give two reasons.

a) poem   _____

b) story/prose   _____

2. *My Favorite Book* is a   Why? Give two reasons.

a) poem   _____

b) story/prose   _____

3. List two differences between a poem and a prose.

a) _____

b) _____

4. List two pairs of rhyming words from *Jack a Nory*.

a) _____   _____

b) _____   _____

5. Who are the characters in *My Favorite Book* besides the narrator?

a) _____

b) _____

c) _____

6. Where did the events in *My Favorite Book* take place?

_____

7. Were you able to guess the ending of *My Favorite Book*? How did you guess?

_____

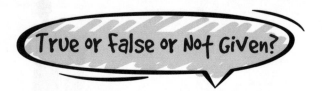

True or False or Not Given?

Read the below statements and say whether the following are true (T), false (F), or the information is not given (NG) in the poem or passage.

	T	F	NG
1 The poem *Jack a Nory* has a story line.			
2 The poem *Jack a Nory* is written from a third person point of view.			
3 *My favorite Book* is narrated in the first person point of view.			
4 *My favorite Book* is written by Joseph Ritson.			
5 In *My favorite Book*, the narrator boxed away the book on purpose.			
6 In *My favorite Book*, the narrator lost his mom recently.			

Elements of Poetry and Prose

Sort the below literary elements into poetry or prose clouds.

grammar/punctuation rules

rhyme

plot

figurative language

rhythm

characters

settings

stanza

dialogs

paragraphs

Poetry

Prose

The Wind and the Sun

Wind and Sun are close friends. They are always together. One day, playfully, they decided to place a bet on who was the stronger of the two.

They decided that whoever gets a passing traveler to take off their overcoat first will win the bet. "Good luck, Windy! You know I'm going to win!" said Sun. Wind replied, "Did you forget who won the last bet?" As they were teasing each other, a woman wearing an overcoat passed by them.

Wind blew hard and fiercely at the traveler, but Wind noticed that the harder it blew the tighter the woman held to her overcoat.

She wrapped it around herself and sprinted[1] across.

When it was the Sun's turn, it gently shined its kind rays. The soft rays spread the warmth over the traveler, and she removed her overcoat.

Sun won the bet and teased Wind saying, "Don't be grumpy now. You can win the next bet."

Moral of the story

People respond better to kind words than yelling!! Here, wind is a metaphor for people who threaten or use rude words. Sun is a metaphor for people who are calm and kind.

---

[1] sprinted: to go at top speed

1. Wind replied, "Did you forget who won the last bet?"

Who won the last bet according to this statement?

a) Wind

b) Sun

c) Author

2. Who is narrating the story?

a) Wind

b) Sun

c) Author

3. Wind noticed that the harder it blew the tighter the woman held to her overcoat.

Why did the woman hold the overcoat tight?

_____

4. Sun won the bet and teased Wind saying, "Don't be grumpy now. You can win the next bet."

Why is being grumpy not the best way to react to a failure?

_____

Is It the Same?

Choose the sentences that use the words in the same meaning as the words used in the story.

1. Wind and Sun are **<u>close</u>** friends.

a) Could you **close** the door?

b) Only **close** relatives are invited to the wedding.

2. **<u>Wind</u>** blew hard and fiercely at the traveler.

a) There is enough **wind** to dry the clothes.

b) Quickly **wind** the yoyo string.

3. One day, playfully, they decided to **<u>place</u>** a bet.

a) This **place** reminds me of the time my cousin came to visit us.

b) Please **place** your orders online.

4. A woman wearing an overcoat **<u>passed</u>** by them.

a) The boarding **pass** was in the bag.

b) If you **pass** the kitchen, could you grab me some water?

Did You Know?

More English words begin with the letter "s."

Verify this using a dictionary, and find the next letter that has more dictionary entries than any other letter.

Reading: Informational Text

Why Do We Eat?

Humans need energy[1] to work. We get energy from food. We eat plants and animals to get energy and nutrition[2]. Plants and animals also need food to grow. Plants get energy from sunlight, and that energy is transferred[3] to us when we eat the plants.

Fruits and vegetables are the best snack as they are produced by plants. They are juicy, tasty, and healthy.

Children and adults do many tasks in a day. Children go to school, learn, play, exercise, and do household chores. Adults go to work, teach their children, exercise, and do many household chores such as cooking, cleaning, and washing. To do all these tasks, we need energy.

What else needs energy besides us? Machines that we use at home also need energy. For example, a car that takes us to places needs fuel to run. A washing machine that washes our clothes needs electricity for energy.

Energy received from food, fuel, and electricity is used every time a human or a machine works. For example, a mobile phone's battery gets drained as we keep using it.

So, once the energy is used up, we need to refill. That's when we feel hunger. Our stomach signals the brain that the energy is consumed[4] and we need to intake more energy. This cycle of taking in energy and using it up goes on and on.

[1] energy: power/strength; [2] nutrition: food necessary for growth;
[3] transferred: move from one place to another; [4] consumed: to use

Understanding the Text

Read the questions and answer.

1. Why do we eat?

_____

2. Why are fruits the best snack?

_____

3. Give an example from the passage for a source of energy and an object that consumes the energy.

_____

4. For humans, the stomach signals refill as hunger. How do we know when a phone or a car needs a refill?

_____

Make a List

List the activities done by children and adults in your household.

Children

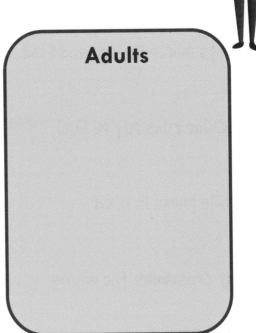

Adults

List 5 food items that you eat every day. Put a check mark (✔) if they are healthy and a cross (✘) if they are unhealthy.

	food items	✔/✘
1.		
2.		
3.		
4.		
5.		

prepaze

Find the Match

Match the cause and effect items on both sides based on the passage.

1. plants and animals need food   brain receives the signal

2. machine runs out of fuel   battery gets drained

3. mobile phone is used   to grow

4. body consumes the energy   needs to be refilled

Food for Thought!

1. We need energy to function. A machine also needs energy to function. Does that make humans a machine?

_____

2. Look around your house and write an example of an object and its source of energy.

_____

3. What will happen if we don't feel hunger?

_____

Work as a Detective

Time to wear a detective's hat! Figure out where the writer has hidden the clues for the underlined words and put them in the evidence box.

1. Plants get energy from sunlight, and that energy is **transferred** to us when we eat the plants.

2. Adults go to work, teach their children, exercise, and do many household **chores** such as cooking, cleaning, and washing.

3. Our stomach signals the brain that the energy is **consumed** and we need more energy. This cycle of taking in energy and using it up goes on and on.

Evidence box	
Meaning	**Clue Words**
1.	
2.	
3.	

This graph is developed using the data collected regarding bullying from 10 different schools. The children were surveyed anonymously.

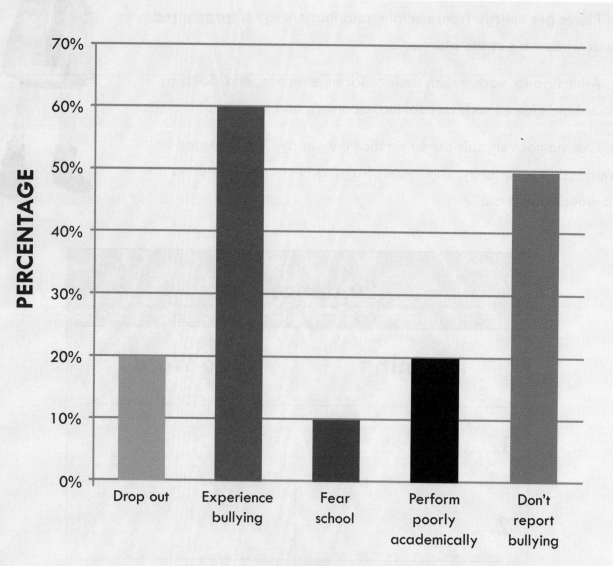

Data Analysis

1. According to the graph, what percentage of children have been bullied?

   _____

2. Which two categories have the same percentage of victims?

   _____ and _____

3. _____ children refuse to go to school every day for fear of being bullied.

4. What percentage of children don't report bullying?

5. Why do you think children don't report bullying?

   _____

Transfer Data

Refer to the graph and complete the below table. List the categories on the left and the corresponding data values on the right.

Categories	Percentage

Riddle

Which is the longest English word without the vowels a, e, i, o, u?

Writing

Write a 3-para essay describing your family members.

 Planning

In the cluster below, write the family member names and your relation to them in the green circles. In the red circles branching from each relation, describe their appearance and the things you like/dislike about them.

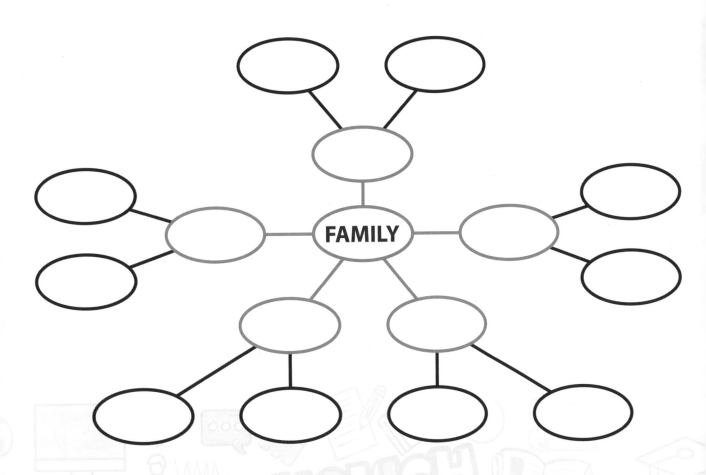

FAMILY

81

prepaze

Step 2 Drafting

Write the essay on My Family with the ideas gathered in the planning stage.

Edit the draft for changes in ideas, grammar, punctuation, and word choice. You can make the changes in a different color pen.

Checklist

◯ Do I have a catchy title?

◯ Does my introduction catch the reader's attention?

◯ Is there any gap in the writing?

◯ Is the verb tense consistent throughtout the writing?

◯ Are the punctuation marks correctly used in statements and dialogs?

◯ Is there repetition of words or ideas?

◯ Are the grammar and spelling mistakes checked?

◯ Have I capitalized letters that need to be capitalized?

◯ Have I used varied sentence structure?

◯ Are there fragments or run-on sentences?

Step 4 — Revision

Write the revised draft here with the changes. Feel free to change ideas and sentences.

Show your work to your parents/siblings and get their feedback. Take both the positive and negative feedback in the same way. Both will help you improve!

Follow this 5-step process for all your writing assignments.

Is it important to be kind to others? Give your opinion on being kind.

Include the following in your essay:

- **Title**

- **Introduction paragraph:** explaining why and how we need to be kind

- **Two body paragraphs:** give an example in each body paragraph

- **Conclusion paragraph:** restate your opinion and leave an advice for the readers

Time to wear an author's hat!

- Decide the theme and point of view. Are you going to be the narrator and also a character in the story?

- Establish a setting.

- Make sure the story has a clear beginning, middle, and end.

- What is the moral of the story?

- Add a title.

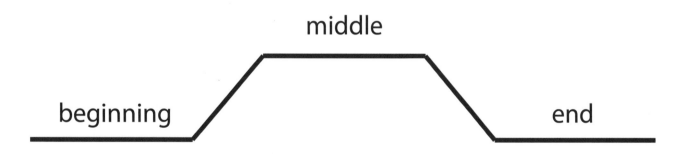

middle

beginning

end

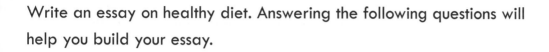

Write an essay on healthy diet. Answering the following questions will help you build your essay.

1. What is a healthy diet?

2. What are a few examples for nutritional food?

3. Why do we need to eat healthy food?

4. How has healthy food helped you grow stronger?

5. Should others follow a healthy diet?

Don't forget a title, and remember that an interesting title will give the readers a great start!

Time to wear a researcher's hat!

Prepare 5 or more survey questions on how often people around you have been a victim of (or witnessed) bullying.

Questions could be on: how bullying affected them or the victims, what they did to stop it, etc.

With all the responses you have gathered, determine an effective way to fight bullying and write it under "Survey result."

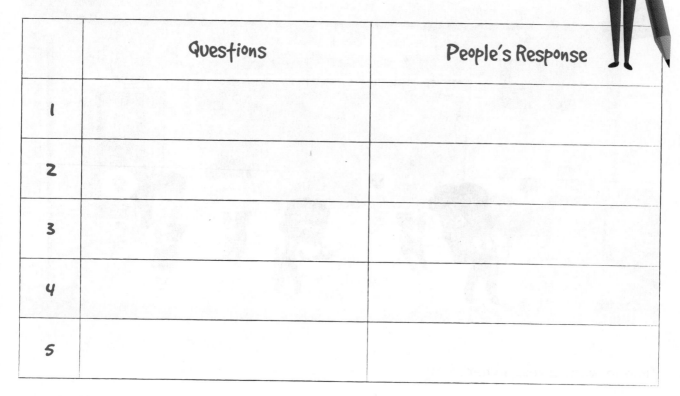

	Questions	People's Response
1		
2		
3		
4		
5		

Survey result:

_____

_____

_____

_____

_____

Storyboard

Time to tell a story in pictures. Recall all the comics and story books you have ever read.

- Think of a theme for your story.

- Write a story, and divide the story into 8 scenes with actions.

- Draw descriptive pictures for each scene and color them.

- Add dialogs or words if required.

- Don't forget a title for your story.

Title	
<u>**Scene 1**</u>	<u>**Scene 2**</u>

prepaze

Scene 3

Scene 4

Scene 5

Scene 6

Scene 7	Scene 8

Did You Know?

"Dreamt" is the only word in English that ends with the letters "-mt."

Can you think of any other word ending in -mt, which is not a variant of dreamt such as "undreamt"?

Math

Use this book to enable your children to explore numbers by solving interesting puzzles and real-life problems. Engage your children with fun, colorful activities and let them fall in love with Math.

Factors and Multiples

Factors are numbers that are multiplied together to get the other number. Factors give us a way to break down a number into smaller numbers.

Example

8 can be obtained by multiplying 2 and 4. $8 = 2 \times 4$. So 2 and 4 are two of the factors of 8.

The factors of 8 are 1, 2, 4, 8

A **multiple** is a number that is obtained by multiplying a number with a whole number.

Example

Let's take the number 3. When we multiply 3 by 2, we get 6. $3 \times 2 = 6$. So 6 is a multiple of 3.

The multiples of 3 are 3, 6, 9, 12, 15, 18, 21, 24, 27, 30, 33 and so on.

Identifying Factors and Multiples

Froggy Loves Numbers!

a. In the mornings, Froggy will jump on the leaves with numbers that are multiples of 5 between 5 and 50. Write them on the leaves and help him jump.

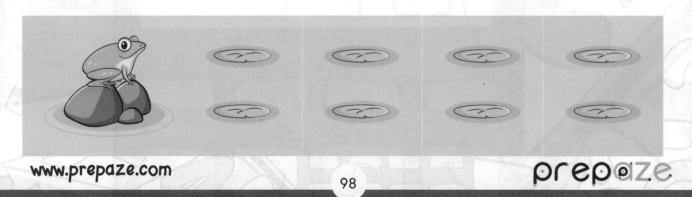

b. At noon, Froggy will jump only on the leaves with numbers that have 36 as its multiple. Write them on the leaves and help him jump.

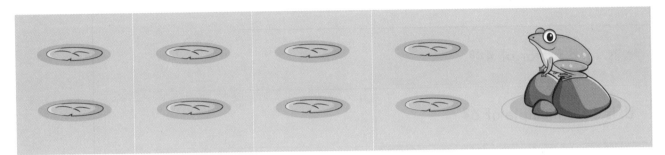

c. In the evenings, Froggy will jump only on the leaves with numbers that are factors of 22. Write them on the leaves and help him jump.

prepaze

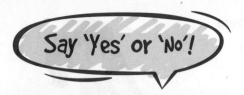

a. Is 12 a multiple of 3?	
b. Is 44 a factor of 4?	
c. Is 11 a factor of 44?	
d. Is 56 a multiple of 6?	
e. Is 4 a factor of 12?	

Can You Number the Rail cars?

The railcars are numbered in multiples of a particular number. The number and few of its multiples are given. Write the remaining numbers on the railcars.

a.

b.

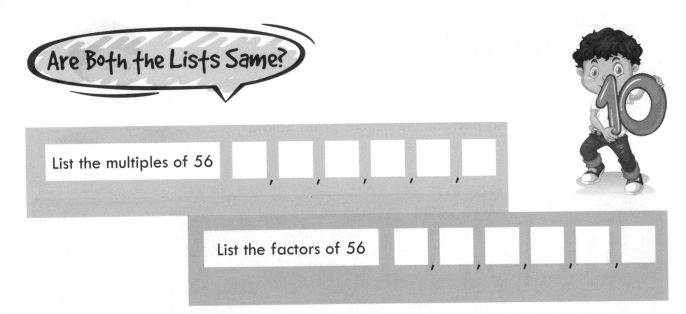

List the multiples of 56 ☐ , ☐ , ☐ , ☐ , ☐ , ☐

List the factors of 56 ☐ , ☐ , ☐ , ☐ , ☐

Are the two lists A and B the same?

☐ Yes   ☐ No

Prime and Composite Numbers

A number that is greater than 1 which can be divided only by itself and that cannot be made by multiplying other numbers is called a **Prime Number**. Number other than prime numbers are called **Composite Numbers**.

The prime numbers have only two factors, the number itself and the number 1.

Example

7 is a prime number.

The only factors of 7 are 1 and 7 itself.

6 is a composite number.

The factors of 6 are 1, 2, 3, and 6.

All whole numbers above 1 are either composite or prime.

Look at the calendar and perform the actions given below.

DECEMBER   2019

S	M	T	W	T	F	S
1	2	3	4	5	6	7
8	9	10	11	12	13	14
15	16	17	18	19	20	21
22	23	24	25	26	27	28
29	30	31				

a. Cross all the composite numbers.

b. Circle all the prime numbers.

c. List the remaining numbers: _____ .

Prime or composite?

Look at the objects below in each set. Write P if the number of objects in the given set is a prime number. Write C if it is a composite number.

a.

b.

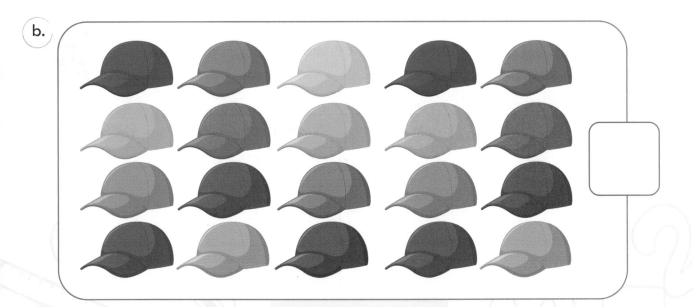

c.

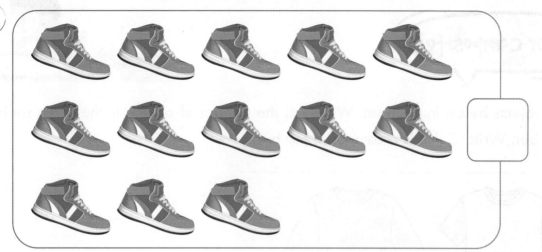

d.

Solve the expressions and say if the answer is Prime or Composite? Write the factors of the answer.

Expression	Answer	Prime or Composite	Factors
a. 8 x 6			
b. 125 ÷ 5			
c. 44 ÷ 4			
d. 20 + 15 +6 +2			
e. 12 x 4			

Solve the following:

a. Parker has $33 to buy icecreams. The cost of each ice cream is a multiple of 5. How many ice creams can she possibly buy?

b. The movie tickets are priced at $2, $3 or $4. What are the possible prices of tickets that Stella would have bought if she spent a total of $16?

c. George has a collection of toy cars. If he arranges his cars in multiples of 4, he can fill 6 rows. How many cars does he own in all?

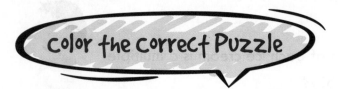

Color the correct Puzzle

Color the puzzle that has factors of 18.

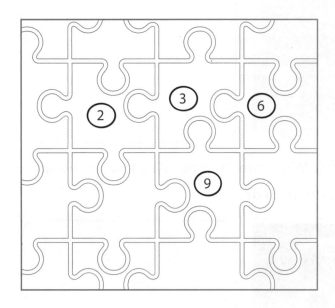

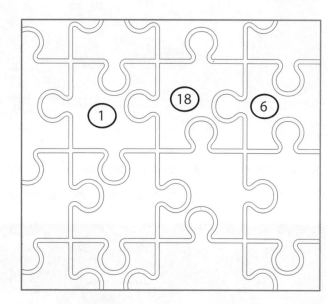

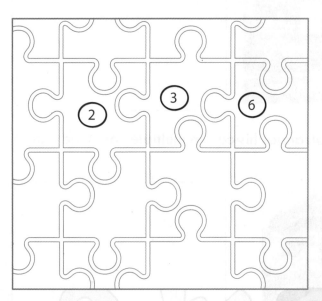

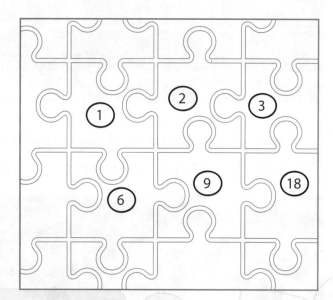

Quiz Time

Rihana is participating in a math online quiz. Help her choose the correct answer.

a.

Which number is not a multiple of 2, 4, and 12?

Option A — 8

Option B — 24

Option C — 48

Option D — 96

b.

Which number is not a factor of 36?

Option A 4

Option B 1

Option C 13

Option D 8

c.

Which number is not a multiple of 6?

Option A 36

Option B 70

Option C 60

Option D 18

d.

Which number is a factor of 18 but not a multiple of 3?

Option A 6

Option B 9

Option C 3

Option D 2

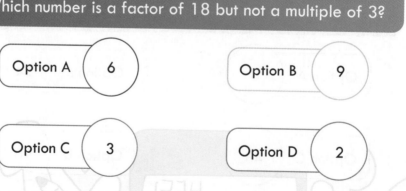

Choose the Correct Answer

Choose the correct answer.

Fact	Option 1	Option 2
a. A composite number whose factors are all prime numbers except 1 and the number itself.	14	16
b. The number that is neither prime nor composite.	5	1
c. A prime number has only two factors.	Yes	No
d. A factor of the number 12 but not a multiple of 2.	3	4
e. All prime numbers are odd numbers.	Yes	No
f. The multiples of a prime number are all prime numbers.	Yes	No

a. List all the prime numbers between 15 and 45.

b. List all composite numbers between 15 and 45.

a. Write all the factors of the number 60.

b. Using the factors for the number 60, write four multiplicative statements that result in the number 60.

$\boxed{} \times \boxed{} = \boxed{}$ $\boxed{} \times \boxed{} = \boxed{}$

$\boxed{} \times \boxed{} = \boxed{}$ $\boxed{} \times \boxed{} = \boxed{}$

Write the multiplication statements for the arrays shown below

a.

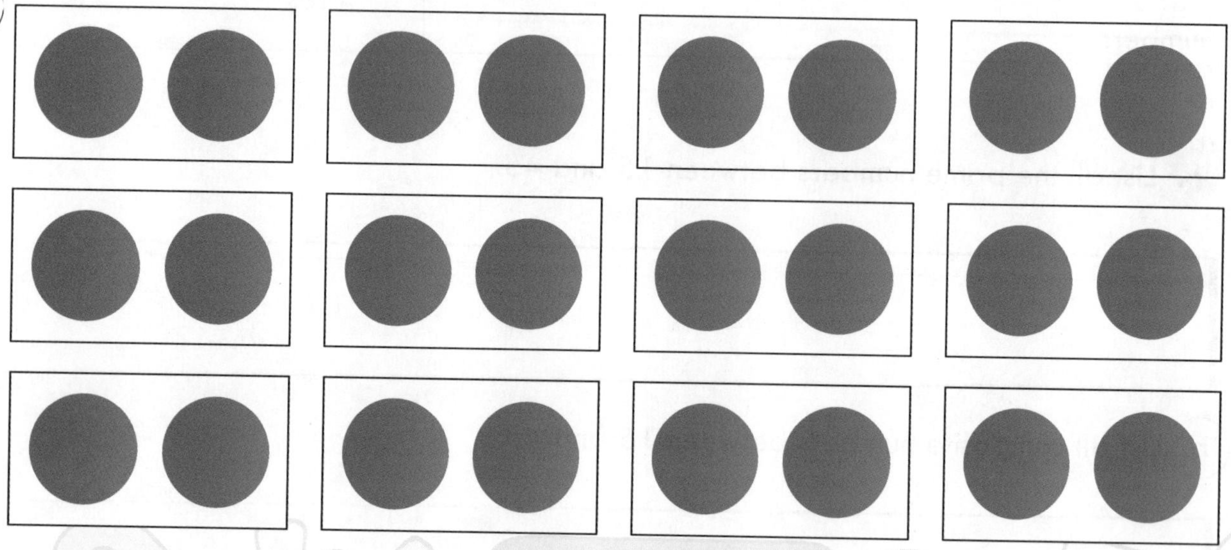

$\boxed{} \times \boxed{} = \boxed{}$

prepaze

b.

□ × □ = □

Factor Tree

a. Complete the factor tree to find the prime factors of 42.

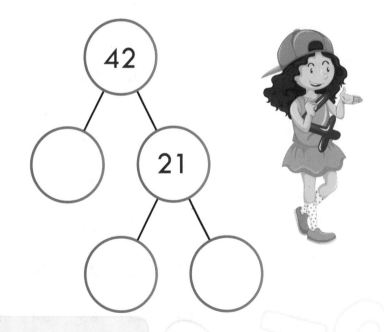

42 = □ × □ × □

b. How do we know that the factor tree given above cannot have any more branches? Explain.

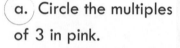

Different Shades of Factors and Multiples

Use the chart below to answer the questions that follow:

a. Circle the multiples of 3 in pink.

b. Cross the multiples of 5 in red.

c. Tick the multiples of 2 in yellow.

d. Circle the multiples of 10 in green.

e. Cross the multiples of 6 in blue.

1	2	3	4	5	6	7	8	9	10
11	12	13	14	15	16	17	18	19	20
21	22	23	24	25	26	27	28	29	30
31	32	33	34	35	36	37	38	39	40
41	42	43	44	45	46	47	48	49	50
51	52	53	54	55	56	57	58	59	60
61	62	63	64	65	66	67	68	69	70
71	72	73	74	75	76	77	78	79	80
81	82	83	84	85	86	87	88	89	90
91	92	93	94	95	96	97	98	99	100

Solve the following.

a. List the numbers that are multiples of 3 but are not factors of 15 and are less than 35.

b. Write all the numbers that are factors of 60 but are not multiples of 6.

c. List all numbers that are factors of 84 and are also the multiple of 7.

There are 48 students in Grade 4.

a. The teacher wants 4 students to sit at each table. How many tables will the class need? Explain using illustrations.

b. During the PE hour, the teacher wants to divide students into groups with a minimum of 2 students. How many different ways can the students be divided into groups? Explain using illustrations.

c. If 1 student drops out of the class, will it be possible to divide the class into equal groups with no remaining students? Explain your answer.

Prime Factors

a. Find the prime factors of 12 and 18. Use them to find out the biggest number that can divide both 12 and 18.

Factors of 12 =

Factors of 18 =

Common Factors of 12 and 18 =

The biggest number that can divide both 12 and 18 =

b. The prime factors of a number are 2, 2, 2, and 7. What is the number?

c. Any number that ends with 0 or 5, will always have 2 and 5 as its factors. True or false? Explain your reasoning with examples.

Complete the Venn Diagram by listing a minimum of 5 numbers on each side. List a minimum of 2 numbers in the common region.

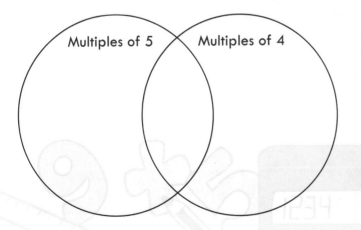

Multiples of 5   Multiples of 4

Multi-Digit Numbers

Miss. Liu's Math Lab

Miss. Liu is explaining that 9 x 4 = 36 can be defined in other terms by comparing the numbers in the equation. She then poses the following questions on the board. Fill in the blanks as appropriate.

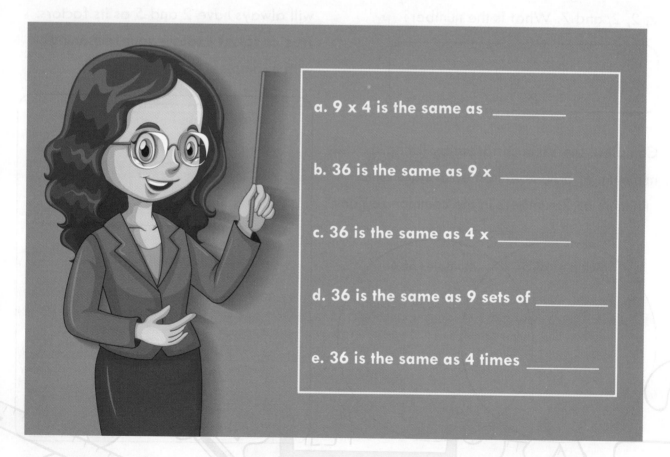

a. 9 x 4 is the same as _____

b. 36 is the same as 9 x _____

c. 36 is the same as 4 x _____

d. 36 is the same as 9 sets of _____

e. 36 is the same as 4 times _____

Select all the correct options.

a. 40 is 8 times as many as 5

b. 8 is 40 times as many as 5

c. 40 is 5 times as many as 8

d. 40 is the same as 8 sets of 5

e. 5 is 8 times as many as 40

George's Assignment

Help George complete his math assignment.

_____ ☐ ☐ ☐

a) 18 is 2 times as many as _____

b) 35 is ___ times as many as 7.

c) 12 is _____ times as many as 3

d) 4 times as many as 8 is _____

e) 6 times as many as 4 is _____

f) 90 is ____ times as many as 9

prepaze

Solve the following problems.

a. John has 7 times more marbles than Peter. Peter has 4 marbles. How many marbles does John have?

b. Greg baked 6 times the number of cupcakes than Jenny. If Jenny baked 3 cupcakes, how many cupcakes did Greg bake?

c. A frog can go 8 inches in one leap. A kangaroo can go 3 times as long as the frog. How far does the kangaroo go in one leap?

d. Steve had 6 fiction books and 18 non-fiction books. How many times more non-fiction books does Steve have than fiction books?

e. Stella has a ribbon that is 20 feet long. The ribbon is 5 times more than the skipping rope that she has. How long is the skipping rope?

 **Solve the Expressions**

Solve the expressions and write the answer in standard form. Also write their word form.

Expression	Standard form	Word form
6 tens + 4 tens		
2 hundreds + 3 hundreds		
6 thousands + 1 thousand		
4 thousands + 11 hundreds		
5 hundreds + 7 tens		

Place Value of Multi-Digit Numbers

Place Value Chart

Use the place value chart to answer the questions below.

a. Label the units on the place value chart above.

b. Express the number 500,000 + 40,000 + 3,000 + 20 + 4 in the place value chart above.

c. Express the number in standard form.

d. Express the number in word form.

Solve the following:

a. A plane goes 800 miles in one hour. A bike goes 40 miles in an hour. By how many times is the plane faster than the bike?

800 miles in one hour

40 miles in one hour

b. Ava has sold 3 tickets for the school fundraising. Brett has sold 24 tickets. How many times more tickets did Brett sell than Ava?

c. A tank holds 540 liters of water. A jug holds 2 liters of water. How many times more water does the tank hold than the jug?

Look at the two sets A and B below and answer the following:

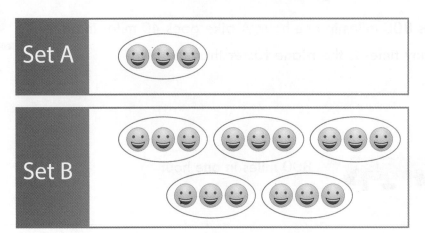

a. Set B has _____ times more smileys than set A.

b. Write an equation to show the number of smileys in Set B.

Daisy has 5 apples.

a. If Jack has 4 more apples than Daisy, how many apples does he have? Write the equation and explain with the help of a diagram.

b. If Steve has 4 times as many apples as Daisy, how many apples does Steve have? Write the equation and explain with the help of a diagram.

Solve the Word Problems

Solve the following:

a. Kate is packing cupcakes for a party. She packs 4 cupcakes in each box. She has 35 cupcakes and 8 boxes. How many cupcakes will be left out?

b. Matt bought 5 pencils for $15. Joe has $19 dollars and he wants to buy 7 pencils. By how much is Joe short?

Solve the following problems.

a. Ken runs 3 miles on Monday and 2 miles on Tuesday. If he wants to run a total of 15 miles that week, how many more miles does he have to run?

b. John earns money by mowing lawns. He earned $6 yesterday. Today he earned half the amount of what he earned yesterday. Last week, he earned $15. He wants to buy a concert ticket that costs $45. How much more money does he have to save?

c. The Oliver girls sold 8 cookies and 9 cupcakes on Monday. They sold 10 cookies and 5 cupcakes on Tuesday. If the cost of each cookie is $2 and that of each cupcake is $3, how much money did they make in all?

Two-Step Equations

Explain your answer with the help of two-step equations and illustrations.

a. There are 4 stars in Set A. Set B has 8 times more than set A. Five more stars are added to Set B. How many stars are now there in Set B?

b. Adrian has 5 times more marbles than his sister, Ava. Ava has 9 marbles. Adrian gives 3 marbles to his sister. How many marbles does Adrian have in total?

Joseph's Toy Car

Joseph has $86. He buys toy cars that cost $12 each.

He writes the following equation to explain his purchase.

$$86 \div 12 = 7 \text{ r } 2$$

a. What does the number 7 represent in the above equation? _____

b. What does the number 2 represent in the above equation? _____

Adam Goes Shopping

Select the statements that represent $48 = 4 \times 12$. Put a tick mark to the correct statement.

☐ Adam bought 4 cartons each containing a dozen balls.

☐ Adam had 12 cars and bought 4 more cars.

☐ Adam bought 4 packets of crayons and each
packet contained 48 crayons.

☐ For 4 years, Adam bought 12 candles each year.

☐ Adam had 48 teddies and gave 12 away.

Solve the word problems.

a. Johnny has 3 times as many pens as markers. The total number of pens and markers is 20. How many pens does he have?

b. Johnny has 2 times as many stamps as his sticker collection. The total number of stamps and stickers is 24. How many stamps does he have?

c. Johnny has 4 times as many pencils as Trent. Trent has 4 pencils. How many pencils does Johnny have?

Tick the correct Answer

Tick the correct answer.

a. Which equation represents the statement "54 is 9 times as many as 6"?

☐ 9 + 6 = 54

☐ 9 x 54 = 6

☐ 54 = 9 x 6

☐ 54 = 9 – 6

b. Which statement is true about the equation 23 - 2 = m - 5?

☐ The value of m is 7 more than 23

☐ The value of m is 7 less than 23

☐ The value of m is 3 more than 23

☐ The value of m is 5 more than 23

prepaze

Ava Bakes for Fundraising

Ava is baking cookies for the school fundraising.
Each baking tray can hold 8 cookies.

Answer the following:

a. If Ava bakes 6 trays of cookies, how many cookies will she bake in all?

b. Ava's mom can bake 3 times as many cookies as what Ava did. How many cookies will Ava's mom bake?

c. If Ava packs her cookies in packs of 4 cookies per pack, how many packages can she make?

d. If Ava charges $5 for one pack of cookies, how much money will she raise for the fundraising if she sells all the cookie packages?

Complete the table below:

Standard form	Expanded form	Word form
305,121		
		Three thousand, five hundred five
	2,000 + 500 + 80 + 9	
	10, 000 + 3,000 + 7	
67, 280		

Stella, Bob, or Zoe?

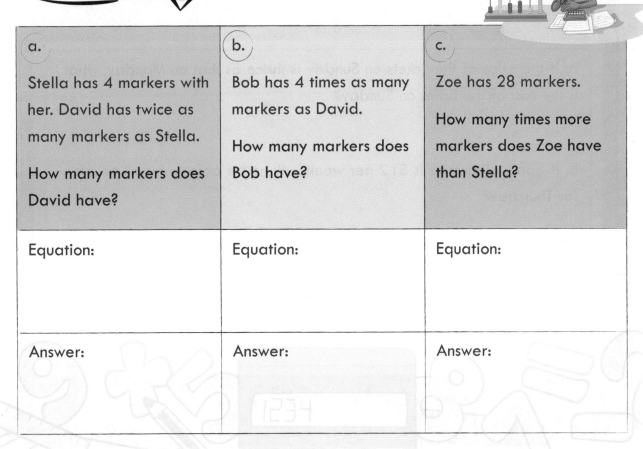

a.	b.	c.
Stella has 4 markers with her. David has twice as many markers as Stella. How many markers does David have?	Bob has 4 times as many markers as David. How many markers does Bob have?	Zoe has 28 markers. How many times more markers does Zoe have than Stella?
Equation:	Equation:	Equation:
Answer:	Answer:	Answer:

prepaze

The price of the Movie tickets in the theatre near Sam's house is different for each day of the week.

$3
MONDAY

$4
TUESDAY

$4.50
WEDNESDAY

$3.50
THURSDAY

$6
FRIDAY

$8
SATURDAY

CINEMA

a. If the price of the tickets on Sunday is thrice as that on Monday, what is the cost of the ticket on Sunday?

b. If Sam's allowance is $12 per week, will he be able to buy 3 tickets for Thursday?

c. Sam wants to treat his mom and dad with tickets for the Saturday show, If he has $10 with him, how much more does he need?

★ MOVIE TIME ★

d. By how many times is the ticket on Saturday more than a ticket on Tuesday?

e. By how many times is the ticket on Monday less than that of a ticket on Friday?

f. If Sam buys 3 tickets on Wednesday, 4 on Friday and 1 on Thursday how much money spend in all?

g. Sam has $15. If he buys two tickets for the Friday show, how much money will he be left with?

Solve the word problems.

a.

Gina bought 4 vases and 6 bouquets for $48.

Each vase costs the same amount.

Each bouquet costs the same amount.

The price of a vase is $3.

What is the price of one bouquet?

The price of one bouquet = $ ☐

b.

Ana bought 5 vases and 7 bouquets for $60 - $80

Each vase costs the same amount.

Each bouquet costs the same amount.

The price of a vase is $6.

What is the least amount spent on the bouquet? $ ☐

What is the most amount spent on the bouquet? $ ☐

prepaze

c.

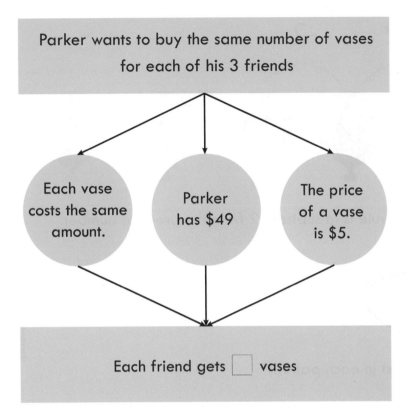

Parker wants to buy the same number of vases for each of his 3 friends

Each vase costs the same amount.

Parker has $49

The price of a vase is $5.

Each friend gets ☐ vases

Patterns

A pattern is a series or sequence of objects, shapes, numbers, or letters that is repeated based on a rule.

A series of numbers that follow a pattern or sequence is called a Number pattern. This pattern generally establishes a common relationship between all numbers.

Examples

In this example, the flowers are arranged in alternating colors of pink and white.

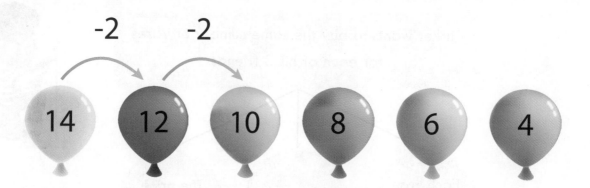

-2   -2

14   12   10   8   6   4

In this example, the rule is to subtract 2 from the previous number.

What Next?

What will come next in each pattern?

a.	
b.	
c.	
d.	

Identify and extend the patterns below.

a.  _____ _____ _____

b. 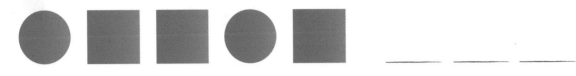 _____ _____ _____

c. 6 5 4 6 5 _____ _____ _____

d. 3 3 2 3 3 _____ _____ _____

Write the missing number.

a. 7, 14, 21, [____] , 35, 42

b. 8, 10, 14, 20, [____] , 38, 50

c. 3, 15, 75, 375, [____]

a. Brett is placing flowers in a vase. In the first vase, he puts 2 flowers. In the next, he puts 4 flowers. He then puts 6 flowers and 8 flowers in the third and fourth vases respectively. If the pattern continues, how many flowers will be there in the sixth vase? Circle the correct answer.

10   12   14   18

b. Nancy is sorting seeds into packets. In the first packet she adds 3 seeds. 9 seeds in the second and 27 seeds in the third. If the pattern continues, how many seeds can we find in the next packet?

60   36   54   81

first five

a. Start at the number 3. Add 6 each time. Write the first five terms in this pattern.

b. Start at the number 72. Subtract 9 each time. Write the first five terms in this pattern.

prepaze

c. Start at number 2. Multiply it by the same number. Write the first five terms in this pattern.

Rules, Rules and More Rules

a. Which rule describes the pattern below:

$$27, 39, 51, 63, 75, 97$$

☐ Add 15

☐ Multiply by 4

☐ Add 12

☐ Add 17

b. In the pattern below, select the statement that describes the 9th term.

$$5, 10, 15, 20,..........$$

☐ The number is an even number

☐ The number is a multiple of 9

☐ The number is greater than 50

a. Circle the sequence below that follows the rule of adding 10?

| 10, 30, 50, 70, 90 | 12, 22, 32, 42, 52 | 5, 10, 15, 20, 25 |

b. Circle the sequence below that follows the rule of adding 6?

| 14, 20, 26, 32, 38 | 1, 4, 6, 9, 16, 25 | 23, 26, 29, 32, 35 |

Match the rule to the pattern.

Rule	Pattern
a. Multiply 4	90, 85, 80, 75, 70
b. Add 11	1, 4, 16, 64, 256
c. Subtract 5	88, 44, 22, 11
d. Divide by 2	1, 12, 23, 34, 45, 56
e. Add 7	7, 14, 21, 28, 35, 42

Draw the next shape in the below patterns:

a.

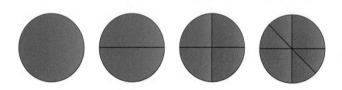
b.

complete the Pattern

Determine which numbers best complete the patterns below:

a.

| 30 | 36 | 42 | 48 | 54 | | |

| 60, 66 | 62, 64 | 70, 76 |

b.

| 55 | 50 | 45 | 40 | 35 | | |

| 30, 35 | 30, 25 | 25, 20 |

c.

| 49 | 45 | 41 | 37 | 33 | | |

| 30, 34 | 29, 25 | 33, 29 |

139

prepaze

John always buys 2 candies more than his brother Mark.

If the number of candies Mark buys is represented as 'm' and the number of candies John buys is represented as 'j', then j = m + 2.

Using this information, complete the table below:

m	j
1	3
2	
11	
18	
23	
54	

Describe the Sequence

Which sequence best describes the patterns below?

a.

| A B B C | A A B C | A B C C |

b.

| A B B C | A A B B | A B C C |

What numbers are missing from the pattern?

26, 34, 42, ___ , 58, 66, ___ , 82, ___ , 98

a. 50, 74, 92

b. 50, 74, 90

c. 52, 76, 94

d. 54, 76, 90

If Jerry got 4 cents every day of the week, starting from Monday, solve
the below problems.

a.
On which day
will he have
12 cents?

b.
For how many days
he will have less than
10 cents?

c.
How many dollars will
he have by the end of
Sunday that week?

Shade the shapes to finish the patterns:

a.

b.

c.

The Fruit Bowl Problem

Andrew is arranging fruits in a bowl in a particular order as shown.
He places the fruits in the following order:

apple,	pear,	orange,	orange,	mango

The pattern continues for 3 more times.

a. What will be the twelfth fruit in this pattern?

b. How many oranges would have been laid on the table? _____

c. What will be the last fruit in this pattern?

Input-output

Complete each input and output by identifying the rule that each table follows:

a. Rule: _____

Input	Output
2	4
6	8
10	
	14
	23

b. Rule: _____

Input	Output
3	9
5	25
7	
	16
	81

c. Rule: _____

Input	Output
2	6
	9
0	
1	
	21

A Starry Night

Look at the pattern below. In each step, a row of 3 stars is added. In the first step, there are 3 stars. 6 stars in step 2 and 9 stars in step 3.

STEP 1   STEP 2   STEP 3

a. If the pattern continues, find the total number of stars in each step through step 10.

Step 1	Step 2	Step 3	Step 4	Step 5	Step 6	Step 7	Step 8	Step 9	Step 10
3	6	9							

b. What pattern do the stars above follow?

Representation of Numbers

Numbers can be represented in numeral form, word form and expanded form. To write down the number in the expanded form start from the highest place value and continue until the ones units.

Example

Place value chart of 10,000

Ten thousands	Thousands	Hundreds	Tens	ones
1	0	0	0	0

On the place value chart below, label the units, and represent the numbers. Also write the number in word form and in expanded form.

a.   54,372

Place value chart

Number in word form _____

Number in expanded form _____

b. 154,372

Place value chart

Number in word form _____

Number in expanded form _____

c. 20,903

Place value chart

Number in word form _____

Number in expanded form _____

d. 76,340

Place value chart

Number in word form _____

Number in expanded form _____

prepaze

(e.) 880,536

Place value chart

Number in word form _____

Number in expanded form _____

Match the following.

665,879	Twenty-three thousand eight hundred twenty
134,980	Seventy-six thousand nine hundred
23,820	Six hundred sixty-five thousand eight hundred seventy-nine
407,191	One hundred thirty-four thousand nine hundred eighty
76,900	Four hundred seven thousand one hundred ninety-one

Fill in the blanks.

a. 400,000 + _____ + 70 + 5 = 400,175

b. _____ + 80,000 + 3,000 + _____ + 6 = 183,076

c. 50,000 + 6,000 + 300 + 60 + _____ = 56,365

d. 600,000 + _____ + 5,000 + _____ + 2 = 665,022

e. 10,000 + _____ + 3 = 10,403

f. 40,000 + _____ + 900 + 20 + 4 = 45,924

g. 700,000 + _____ + _____ + 700 + 5 = 777,705

h. _____ + 600 + 40 + 7 = 20,647

i. _____ + 5000 + 8 = 35,008

Fill the blanks with >, < or =.

a. 112,973 _____ 211,764

b. 87,943 _____ 34,980

c. 200,001 _____ 200,001

d. 63,453 _____ 45,900

e. 132,986 _____ 132,764

Who Will Win the Game?

Four friends played a game. The player with the most points wins. Use the information in the table below to order the number of points each player earned from least to greatest. Then, name the person who won the game.

Player Name	Points Earned
Cliff	51,967
Biff	35,693
Ruth	75,968
Eva	48,380

Less Than or Greater Than?

Use each of the digits 6, 0, 3, 5, 1 exactly once to create two different five-digit numbers.

a. Write each number on the line, and compare the two numbers by using the symbols < or >. Write the correct symbol in the circle.

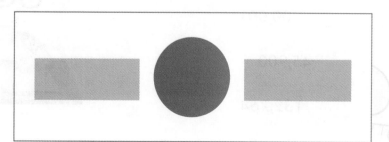

b. Use words to write a comparison statement for the problem above.

Label and Represent

Label and represent the product or quotient on the place value chart.

a. 10 x 5 thousands = _____ thousands = _____

b. 10 x 1 thousands = _____ thousands = _____

c. 6 thousands ÷ 10 = _____ ÷ 10 = _____ hundreds

d. 3 hundreds ÷ 10 = _____ ÷ 10 = _____ tens

Solve for each expression by writing the solution in unit form and in standard form.

Expression	Unit form	Standard form
10 × 4 tens		
9 hundreds x 10		
5 thousands ÷ 10		
4 ten thousands ÷ 10		
10 x 2		
(5 tens 5 ones) x 10		
(3 hundreds 2 tens) x 10		
(6 thousands x 5 hundreds) x 10		
(4 thousands 4 tens) ÷ 10		
(6 ten thousands 9 tens) ÷ 10		

Who Is Right?

The teacher asks the class to write twenty-seven thousand forty-seven.

 **Jessi wrote: 27,047**    **Jance wrote: 27,470**

Which student wrote the correct number?

What mistake did the other student make?

Rounding off

To round off a number, look at the digit to the right of the place to which you are rounding off.

- If the digit is greater than or equal to 5, round up the number.

- If the digit is less than 5, round down the number.

When the number is 5 or greater than 5, we round up.

When the number is less than 5, we round down.

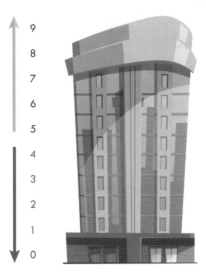

Number Line Rounding off

Complete each statement by rounding the number to the given place value. Use the number line to show your work.

a. 1,700 to the nearest thousand

b. 18,430 to the nearest ten thousand

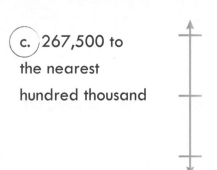

c. 267,500 to the nearest hundred thousand

d. 749,545 to the nearest hundred thousand

Estimate the difference by rounding each number to the given place value.

842,150 – 222,802

a. Round to the nearest ten thousand.

b. Round to the nearest hundred thousand.

Estimate the sum by rounding each number to the given place value.

357,908 + 148,567

a. Round to the nearest ten thousand.

b. Round to the nearest hundred thousand.

Round to the nearest ten thousand.

a. 26,000 ≈

b. 34,920 ≈

c. Explain why two problems have the same answer. Write another number that has the same answer when rounded to the nearest ten thousand.

There are 18,550 BurgerChef outlets around the world. Round the number of outlets to the nearest thousand and ten thousand. Which answer is more accurate? Explain your answer using pictures, numbers, or words.

There are 499,500 employees working in Remo Industries.

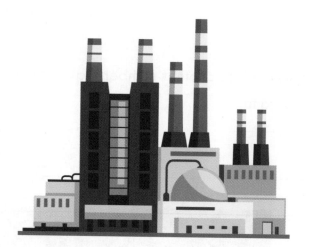 

a. Round the number of employees to the given place value.

   i. Thousands:

   ii. Ten Thousands:

   iii. Hundred Thousands:

b. Explain why two of your answers are the same.

Maria wanted help with the first question on her homework.

The question asked the students to round 328,702 to the nearest thousand and then to explain the answer. Maria thought that the answer was 328,000.

Was her answer correct? How do you know? Use pictures, numbers, or words to explain.

Plot the following numbers in the number line. Use the color codes as given.

| 70 | 438 | 893 |

a. Round each number to the nearest 100. How can you see this on the number line?

b. Round each number to the nearest 1000. How can you see this on the number line?

A bookstore has 56,859 books. Color all the places in the number that have the digit 5.

ones	
Tens	
Hundreds	
Thousands	
Ten thousands	

Dennis wrote 432,098 in expanded form. Color all the values Dennis wrote.

200,000	30,000	4000	900	90	8

Relationship between the Two 6s

Is the relationship between the 6s in 6,672 and the 6s in 76,672 different? Explain your thinking.

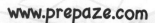

Fill in the blanks with the number names of the given numbers.

a. Macy has 456,340 pebbles with her. That means she has _____

_____ pebbles with.

b. There are at least 180,536 types of animals in the world. This means that there are

_____ types of animals.

c. Kevin has a collection of 11,238 marbles. That means he has a collection of_____

_____ coins.

Which Has More?

Which has more? Choose the correct answer.

a. A room having 123,839 balls or a room having 213,763 pebbles?

b. A factory manufacturing 650,009 cars or a factory manufacturing 609,345 buses?

c. A city with 35,874 people or a city with 26,874 animals?

d. A water tank with 24,145 liters of water or a petrol pump with 19,995 liters of petrol?

Solve the word problems.

a. Jeni saved 3 thousand dollar bills, 6 hundred dollar bills, and 2 ten dollar bills to buy a bike. The bike costs 10 times as much as she has saved. How much does the bike cost?

b. Last year the toy factory experienced downtime and did not manufacture any toys. But this year, the factory produced 45 thousand electronic toys and 9 hundred educational toys, which is 10 times as many toys as last year. How many toys did the factory produce last year?

c. City X has a population of 2 million people. City Y has 2 hundred thousand people.

i. Which city has more population and by how much?

ii. Write a sentence to compare the populations for each city using the words 10 times as many.

d. Lisa collected $850 selling Girl Scout cookies. Lisa's troop collected 10 times as much as she did. How much money did Lisa's troop raise?

prepaze

This number was rounded to the nearest ten thousand. List the possible digits that could go in the thousands place to make this statement correct. Use a number line to show your work. 14_ ,644 ≈ 140,000.

In an adult Marathon, 39,786 men finished the race, and 26,928 women finished the race. Each finisher was given a medal.

a. About how many men's shirts were given away? About how many women's shirts were given away? Give approximate answers and explain how you found your answers.

b. Before the race, the medals had to be ordered. If you were the person in charge of ordering the medals and estimated how many to order by rounding, would you have ordered enough medals? Explain your thinking.

How Heavy Are the Gift Packages?

Draw a tape diagram to represent the problem. Use numbers to solve, and write your answer as a statement.

At Fast track Delivery, gift packages of the following weight arrived.

Package red: 4,887 pounds

Package green: 12,556 pounds

Package blue: 2,677 pounds

Package yellow: 234 pounds

a. What is the combined weight of the Package red and Package green?

b. What is the combined weight of the Package blue and Package green?

c. What is the combined weight of the Package blue and Package yellow?

d. What is the combined weight of all the four packages?

prepaze

A Tale of Two Friends

Estimate and then solve the problem. Model the problem with a tape diagram. Explain if your answer is reasonable.

Debbie and Elsa are best friends. For a bake sale, Debbie baked 149 doughnuts. Elsa baked 44 more doughnuts than Debbie.

a. About how many doughnuts did Debbie and Elsa bake? Estimate by rounding each number to the nearest ten before adding.

b. Exactly how many doughnuts did Debbie and Elsa bake?

c. Is your answer reasonable? Compare your estimate from (a) to your answer from (b). Write a sentence to explain your reasoning.

During the month of March, 68,025 tourists visited an amusement park. If 15,614 tourists visited in the first week of March, how many tourists visited in the rest of the month?

Use the standard algorithm to solve the following subtraction problems.

a. 9,812 - 2,501

b. 17,032 - 3,133

c. 9,072 - 2,561

165

prepaze

Draw a tape diagram to represent the following problem. Use numbers to solve. Write your answer as a statement. Check your answer.

> What number must be added to 2,278 to result in a sum of 7,525?

The population of a city is 638,381. In that population, 18,170 are children.

a. How many adults live in the city?

b. 316,101 of the adults are males. How many adults are female?

Distribute and Solve

Distribute 22 as 20 + 2 and solve - 30 x 22.

Determine the perimeter and area of rectangles A and B.

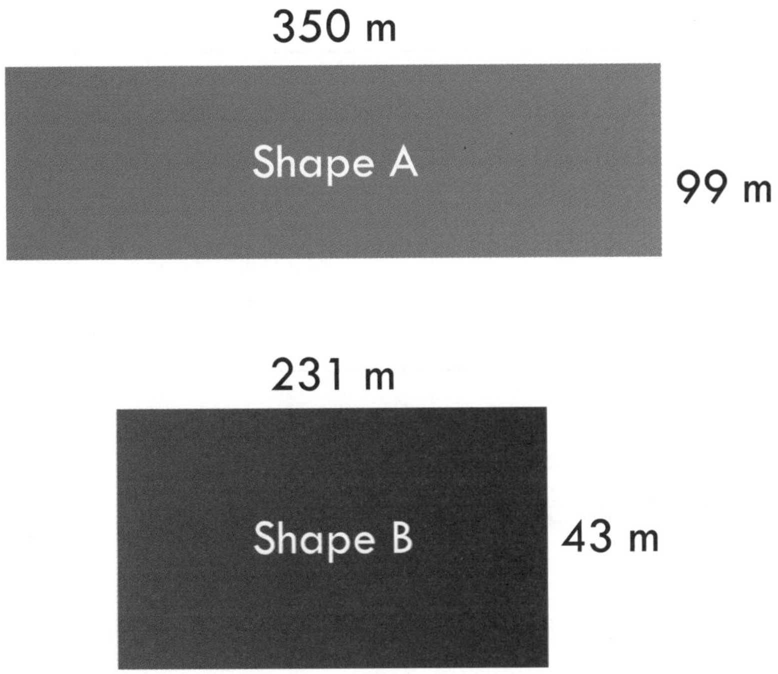

350 m

Shape A

99 m

231 m

Shape B

43 m

Shape A

Shape B

If 30 apples can be packed in a box. How many apples can be packed in 25 boxes.

Divide the following numbers. Check your work by multiplying. Draw disks on a place value chart as needed.

a. 576 ÷ 2

b. 333 ÷ 3

c. 955 ÷ 5

Juicy and Yum Yum

Luke filled 481 one-liter bottles with fruit juice. He distributed the bottles to 4 stores. Each store received the same number of bottles. How many liter bottles did each of the stores receive? Were there any bottles left over? If so, how many?

A truck has 5 crates of oranges. Each crate has an equal number of oranges. Altogether, the truck is carrying 1,725 oranges. How many oranges are in each crate?

Find the quotient and remainder for 2,132 ÷ 3. How could you change the digit in the ones place of the whole so that there would be no remainder? Explain how you determined your answer.

Solve the following problems. Draw tape diagrams to help you solve them. If there is a remainder, shade in a small portion of the tape diagram to represent that portion of the whole.

A tennis court contains 7 sections of seats with the same number of seats in each section. If there are 248 seats, how many seats are in each section?

Anna solved the following division problem by drawing an area model.

	200	30	9
4	800	120	36

a. What division problem did she solve?

b. Show a number bond to represent Anna's area model, and represent the total length using the distributive property.

Decimal Numbers

Fractions that have 10, 100 or 1,000 as denominators are called **Decimal Fractions**.

The fraction $\frac{1}{10}$ is written as 0.1, using a decimal point. The decimal point separates the whole number part from the decimal part. This way of representing fractions is known as **decimal numbers or decimals**.

Whole number   Decimal part

0.1

Decimal point

Read the length of the pencil.

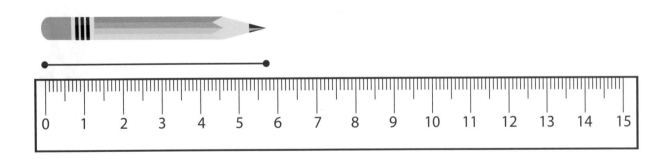

a. The length of the pencil is _____ cm _____ mm.

b. The length can also be written in decimal fractions as ☐

c. The length can also be written in decimal number as ☐

The Confused Clown

A clown is juggling some balls. Some balls have fractions written on them, while others have decimals written on them. Help him match the fractions with the decimals.

 1.2

71.80

0.4

$\dfrac{4}{10}$

$1\dfrac{2}{10}$

$71\dfrac{80}{100}$

Write the decimal for the shaded part.

a.

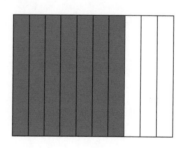

b.

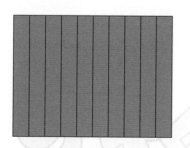

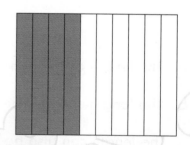

Joel brought a fridge of height $\frac{670}{10}$ inches. He wants to place it inside a cabinet of height $\frac{7200}{100}$ inches. Will the fridge fit into the cabinet?

Building a Math circuit

Rina and her friends are testing a circuit. The bulb with the highest number will light glow brighter when the switch is turned on.

Use Comparison symbols to show which bulb will glow bright when the switch is turned on.

a.

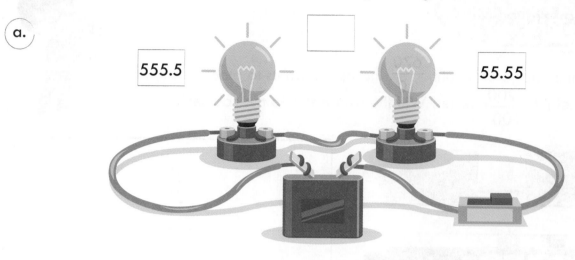

555.5   55.55

b.

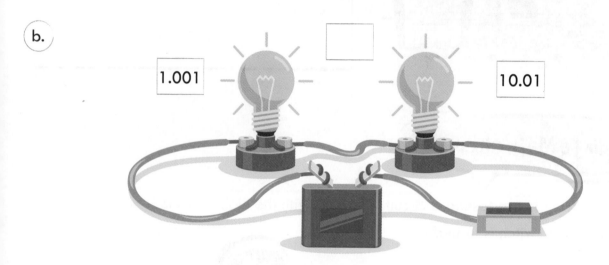

1.001   10.01

c.

16.7   1.76

prepaze

Fractions

Fractions that look different but represent the same amount are called equivalent fractions. Equivalent fractions represent the same part of the whole.

For example, $\frac{1}{2}$ and $\frac{2}{4}$ are equivalent fractions.

Equivalent fractions

Look at the table and answer each question.

c. What fraction is the lemon grass plant? Write an equivalent for it.

a. What fraction is the aloe vera in her garden? Write in the simplest form.

Plant in Ann's Garden

Plant Type	Number of plants
Rose plant	2
Lily plant	4
Aloe vera plant	3
Lemon grass plant	6

b. What fraction is the total of rose plant and lily plant?

The shaded fraction is decomposed into smaller pieces. Write the
equivalent fractions by showing the multiplication. One is done for you.

a.

$$\frac{2}{6} = \frac{2 \times 2}{6 \times 2} = \frac{4}{12}$$

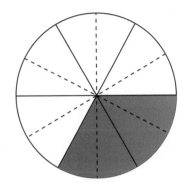

b.

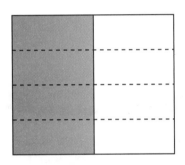

c.

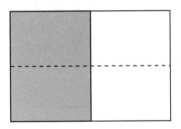

d.

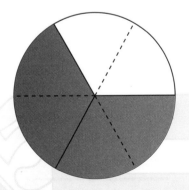

prepaze

Fraction Sort

Look at the fraction pairs. Sort the pairs into equivalent and not equivalent and write them near the appropriate symbols.

| $\dfrac{4}{6}, \dfrac{1}{3}$ | $\dfrac{2}{6}, \dfrac{6}{18}$ | $\dfrac{1}{5}, \dfrac{5}{25}$ | $\dfrac{2}{8}, \dfrac{3}{9}$ |

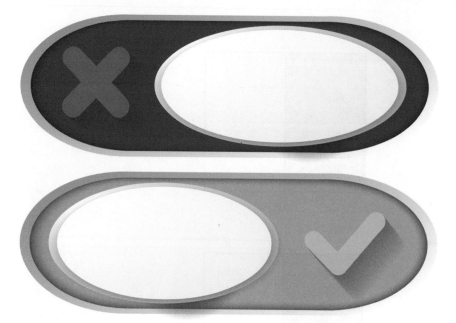

Divide and Conquer

Divide the boxes to show $\dfrac{1}{2}$ is equal to $\dfrac{3}{6}$.

Draw a number line for each of these tape diagrams. Write the fraction for the shaded portion on the number line.

a.

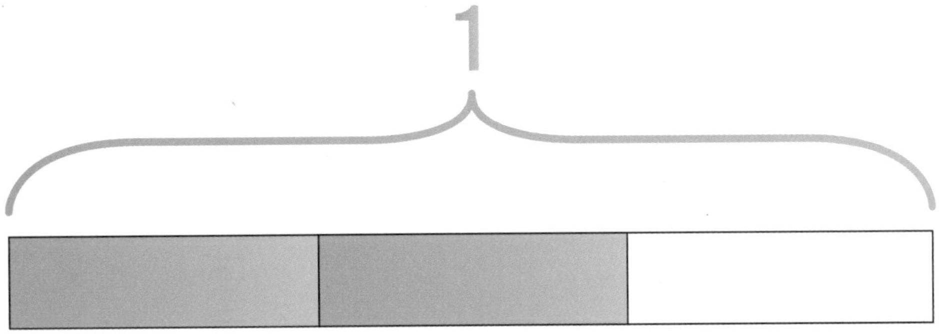

$$1$$

b.

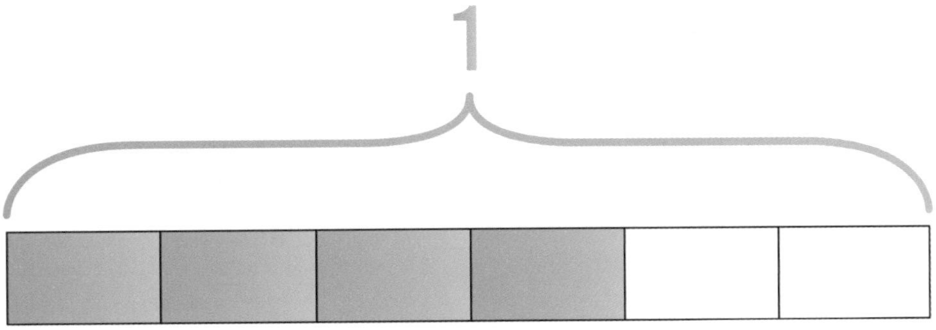

$$1$$

c. Are (a) and (b) equivalent fractions? Show by writing a number sentence using multiplication.

Compare the fractions using >, < and =.

a. $\dfrac{4}{10}$ ☐ $\dfrac{3}{5}$

b. $\dfrac{11}{12}$ ☐ $\dfrac{2}{5}$

c. $\dfrac{7}{16}$ ☐ $\dfrac{51}{100}$

d. $\dfrac{7}{10}$ ☐ $\dfrac{5}{8}$

e. $\dfrac{2}{4}$ ☐ $\dfrac{1}{3}$

f. $\dfrac{1}{2}$ ☐ $\dfrac{3}{4}$

prepaze

Area Model

Draw an area model for each pair of fractions. Compare the two fractions using the symbols >, < or =.

a. $\dfrac{1}{2}$ $\boxed{<}$ $\dfrac{2}{3}$

$\dfrac{1 \times 3}{2 \times 3} = \dfrac{3}{6}$

$\dfrac{2 \times 2}{3 \times 2} = \dfrac{4}{6}$

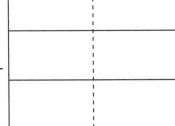

b. $\dfrac{4}{5}$ $\boxed{\phantom{<}}$ $\dfrac{3}{4}$

c. $\dfrac{3}{7}$ $\boxed{\phantom{<}}$ $\dfrac{2}{6}$

d. $\dfrac{3}{5}$ $\boxed{\phantom{<}}$ $\dfrac{4}{7}$

prepaze

a. Plot the following fractions on the number line without measuring.

i. $\dfrac{5}{12}$ 　　　　　ii. $\dfrac{3}{4}$ 　　　　　iii. $\dfrac{2}{6}$

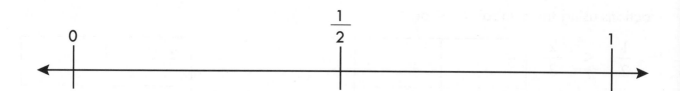

b. Compare the fractions using the symbols >, < or =.

i.

$\dfrac{5}{12}$ ☐ $\dfrac{3}{4}$

ii.

$\dfrac{3}{4}$ ☐ $\dfrac{2}{6}$

c. Explain how you plotted the fractions on the number line.

_____

_____

_____

Solve:

a. $\dfrac{2}{5} + \dfrac{1}{5}$ = _____ 　　　 b. $\dfrac{6}{11} - \dfrac{3}{11}$ = _____ 　　　 c. $\dfrac{8}{15} - \dfrac{6}{15}$ = _____

d. $\dfrac{3}{7} - \dfrac{1}{7}$ = _____ 　　　 e. $\dfrac{3}{8} + \dfrac{5}{8}$ = _____ 　　　 f. $\dfrac{13}{19} + \dfrac{3}{19}$ = _____

Use the following three fractions to write two subtraction sentences and two addition number sentences. One is done for you.

a. $\dfrac{6}{11}$, $\dfrac{15}{11}$, $\dfrac{9}{11}$

$$\dfrac{6}{11} + \dfrac{9}{11} = \dfrac{15}{11}$$

$$\dfrac{9}{11} + \dfrac{6}{11} = \dfrac{15}{11}$$

$$\dfrac{15}{11} - \dfrac{9}{11} = \dfrac{6}{11}$$

$$\dfrac{15}{11} - \dfrac{6}{11} = \dfrac{9}{11}$$

b. $\dfrac{7}{19}$, $\dfrac{13}{19}$, $\dfrac{6}{19}$

c. $\dfrac{5}{13}$, $\dfrac{6}{13}$, $\dfrac{11}{13}$

d. $\dfrac{1}{9}$, $\dfrac{8}{9}$, $\dfrac{9}{9}$

prepaze

Decompose the Sum

Use a number bond to decompose the sum. Record your final answer as a mixed number. One is done for you.

a. $\dfrac{4}{7} + \dfrac{6}{7} = \dfrac{10}{5} = 1\dfrac{3}{7}$ $\dfrac{7}{7} + \dfrac{3}{7}$	b. $\dfrac{8}{11} + \dfrac{5}{11}$
c. $\dfrac{8}{13} + \dfrac{7}{13}$	d. $\dfrac{8}{9} + \dfrac{10}{9}$
e. $\dfrac{11}{4} + \dfrac{7}{4}$	f. $\dfrac{12}{5} + \dfrac{9}{5}$

Decompose the Difference

Use a number bond to decompose the sum. Record your final answer as a mixed number.

a. $\dfrac{16}{7} - \dfrac{8}{7}$	b. $\dfrac{10}{3} - \dfrac{5}{3}$

c. $\dfrac{11}{8} - \dfrac{1}{8}$	d. $\dfrac{15}{6} - \dfrac{2}{6}$
e. $\dfrac{12}{9} - \dfrac{1}{9}$	f. $\dfrac{17}{5} - \dfrac{3}{5}$

Find the Sum

Find the sum. Use a tape diagram to represent each addend. One is done for you.

a. $\dfrac{1}{3} + \dfrac{5}{6}$  $\dfrac{2}{6} + \dfrac{5}{6} = \dfrac{7}{6}$	b. $\dfrac{1}{5} + \dfrac{3}{10}$
c. $\dfrac{5}{12} + \dfrac{1}{6}$	d. $\dfrac{2}{3} + \dfrac{4}{9}$
e. $\dfrac{5}{8} + \dfrac{1}{2}$	f. $\dfrac{1}{6} + \dfrac{7}{12}$

prepaze

Find the Difference.

Find the difference. One is done for you.

---

a. $\dfrac{3}{4} - \dfrac{5}{8}$

$\dfrac{3 \times 2}{4 \times 2} = \dfrac{6}{8}$ $\dfrac{5 \times 1}{8 \times 1} = \dfrac{5}{8}$

$\dfrac{6}{8} - \dfrac{5}{8} = \dfrac{1}{8}$

b. $\dfrac{4}{5} - \dfrac{1}{10}$

---

c. $\dfrac{9}{12} - \dfrac{1}{3}$

d. $\dfrac{2}{3} - \dfrac{1}{9}$

---

e. $\dfrac{3}{5} - \dfrac{1}{2}$

f. $\dfrac{4}{6} - \dfrac{5}{12}$

---

prepaze

Number Line Addition

Draw a number line to model the addition. One is done for you.

a. $\dfrac{3}{5} + \dfrac{7}{10}$

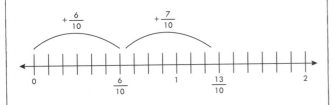

$$\dfrac{3}{5} + \dfrac{7}{10} = \dfrac{13}{10}$$

b. $\dfrac{3}{4} + \dfrac{5}{8}$

c. $\dfrac{5}{6} + \dfrac{1}{12}$

d. $\dfrac{7}{9} + \dfrac{1}{3}$

e. $\dfrac{1}{6} + \dfrac{5}{3}$

f. $\dfrac{2}{9} + \dfrac{4}{3}$

prepaze

Solve. One is done for you.

a.

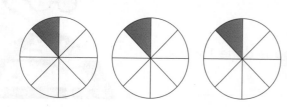

$$\frac{3}{8} = \frac{1}{8} + \frac{1}{8} + \frac{1}{8}$$

$$\frac{3}{8} = 3 \times \frac{1}{8}$$

b.

c. $6 \times \dfrac{1}{7} =$

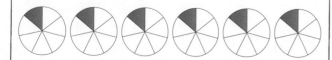

d. $2 \times \dfrac{2}{5} =$

e. $3 \times \dfrac{5}{6} =$

f. $4 \times \dfrac{2}{5} =$

Oreo has 6 chew toys. Milo has $\frac{1}{3}$ as many chew toys as Oreo. How many chew toys does Oreo have?

olivia Likes Dancing

Week 1, Olivia went to dance class 5 times. Each class was 1 hour. Week 2, she went to dance class 4 times. Each class was $\frac{3}{2}$ hours.

Which week did Olivia spend more total time in dance class and by how much?

Draw three different area models to represent one third by shading. Then decompose the shaded portion as

a. Sixths

b. Ninths

c. Twelfths

Write the fraction for each shaded portion and then write them as equivalent fractions for one third.

Find one equivalent fraction for each of the given fractions using multiplication.

a. $\dfrac{4}{6}$	b. $\dfrac{5}{8}$
c. $\dfrac{2}{12}$	d. $\dfrac{2}{7}$

Measurement

Leon Goes to France

Leon is traveling to france. Calculate the total weight of his luggage's.

21 kg 321 g

19 kg 195 g

Weigh Me out

Sofia wants to know how much lighter she is than Layla?

I am Sofia,
I weigh 27 kg

I am Luna,
I weigh 29 kg
121 g

I am Layla,
I weigh 29 kg
119 g

A cricket ball weighs 163 g. How much would 9 such cricket balls weigh? Write your answer in kg and g.

Rony uses half pumpkin to make pumpkin pie. If the pumpkin weighed 2 kg 450 g, how much pumpkin did he use?

Convert the Measurements

I.

a. 1 kg = _____ g

b. 15 kg = _____ g

c. 2 kg 450 g = _____ g

d. _____ kg = 12000 g

e. 7 kg 125 g = _____ g

f. 16 kg _____ g = 16005 g

g. _____ kg _____ g = 4568 g

h. _____ kg = 25000 g

i. 5 kg 55 g = _____ g

j. _____ kg _____ g = 5725 g

II.

a. 2 km = _____ m

b. 6 m = _____ cm

c. _____ km = 15000 m

d. _____ m = 1100 cm

e. 3 km 210 m = _____ m

f. _____ km = 13000 m

g. 4 m 14 cm = _____ cm

h. 81 m = _____ cm

i. 4 km 980 m = _____ m

j. 7 m 18 cm = _____ cm

III.

a. 2 km = _____ m

b. 6 m = _____ cm

c. _____ km = 15000 m

d. _____ m = 1100 cm

e. 3 km 210 m = _____ m

f. _____ km = 13000 m

g. 4 m 14 cm = _____ cm

h. 81 m = _____ cm

i. 4 km 980 m = _____ m

j. 7 m 18 cm = _____ cm

Johnson Builds a Wall

Johnson took 6 days to build a wall. He worked a total of 48 hours. If he divided his work evenly among 6 days, how long did he work each day?

Olivia spends 250 minutes in gymnastics in the first week and 430 minutes in the second week. What is the difference in the amount of time spent between the weeks?

prepaze

Grandma's Colorful Quilt

Emma's grandma wanted to make a colorful quilt. Below are the models of the cut pieces of the fabric she is going to use. Help her find the area (in square inch) of those cut pieces.

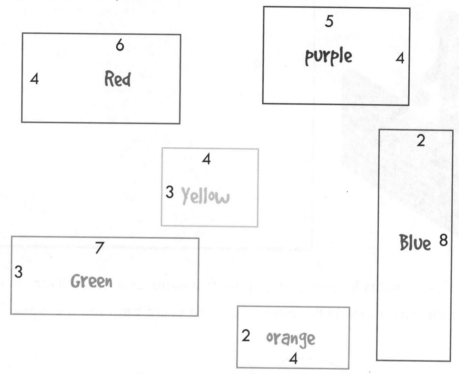

a. Area of red cloth = _____

b. Area of yellow cloth = _____

c. Area of green cloth = _____

d. Area of orange cloth = _____

e. Area of blue cloth = _____

f. Area of purple cloth = _____

g. What is the total area of all the pieces together?

h. The cost of red, yellow, and orange cloth is $3 per square inch cloth. What is the price of red, yellow, and orange cloth altogether?

i. If the cost of the purple cloth is $82.00, what is the cost of purple cloth per inch?

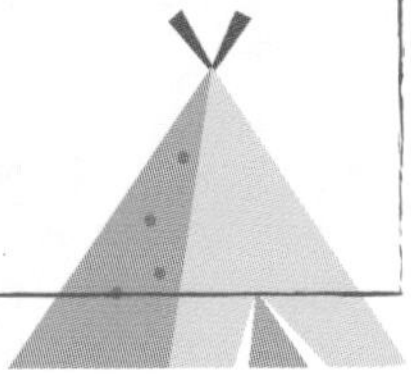

Lily bought 6 cookies, 2 cupcakes and 2 doughnuts from a bakery store. The cost of each item is shown below. If she paid with a $50 bill, how much change should she get?

$2.25 $1.10  $2.00

Given below are the prices of several stationery items.

Items	Cost (in $)
Eraser	2.15
Pen	3.10
Pencil	2.75
Sharpener	2.45
Paper clip box	6.00

Steven had $9.00 when he went to a store. If he bought 1 paper clip box, what is the item he can buy with the money left?

Data

The Pencil Problem

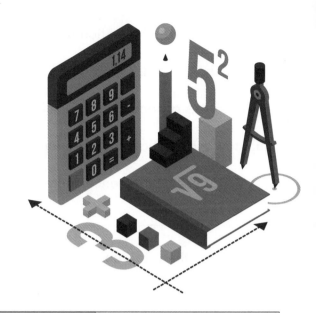

A group of students measured the length of their pencils (in inches). The measurements are shown in the table. Make a line plot to display the data.

Name of the students	Length of the pencil (in inches)
Matte	$3\frac{1}{4}$
Jenny	$3\frac{1}{2}$
Joseph	$2\frac{1}{2}$
Felix	$2\frac{1}{4}$
Fautin	3
Genelia	$2\frac{3}{4}$
Hanna	$3\frac{1}{2}$

Line plot:

Use the above information to solve the problems below.

i) Who has a pencil length 1 inch longer than Felix's?_____

ii) Who has a pencil length 1 inch shorter than Jenny's?_____

iii) How many quarter inches long is Fautin's pencil?_____

iv) What is the difference, in inches, between Joseph's and Genelia's pencil length?

_____

v) What is the total length of Hanna, Fautin's and Jenny's pencil altogether?_____

Ms. Rosaline has 16 jars as shown below. Display the data on the line plot.

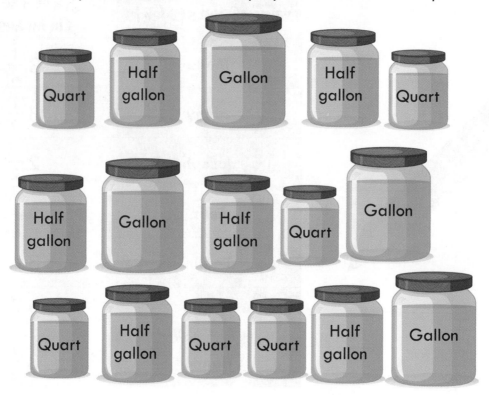

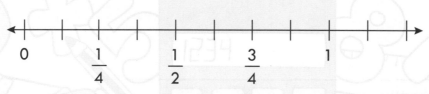

b. Use the above information to solve the problems below.

i. How many jars have a capacity of half-gallon or more? _____

ii. How many jars have a capacity of 1 gallon? _____

iii. How many jars have a capacity of less than 1 quart? _____

iv. Ms. Rosaline emptied all her jars. She wants to pour seven and a half gallons of liquid into them. Will all of her jars hold this amount? Explain your answer.

Use the line plots to answer each question.

a. The line plot below shows the length of girls hair(in feet) in Ms. Rosy's class.

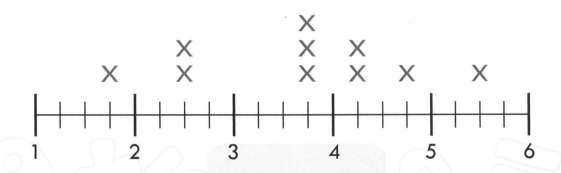

What is the total length of the longest and the shortest hair?

b. The line plot below shows the distance students lived from the school(in miles).

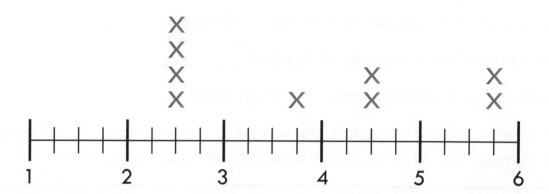

What is the difference between the longest and shortest distance?

c. The line plot shows the size(in inches) of different insect species.

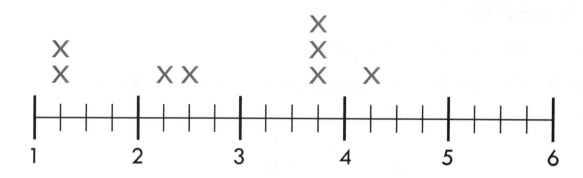

What is the difference between the longest species and the short species of insects?

A Track Plot

A group of grade four students run around a track. The measurements are shown in the table. Draw a line plot to display the data.

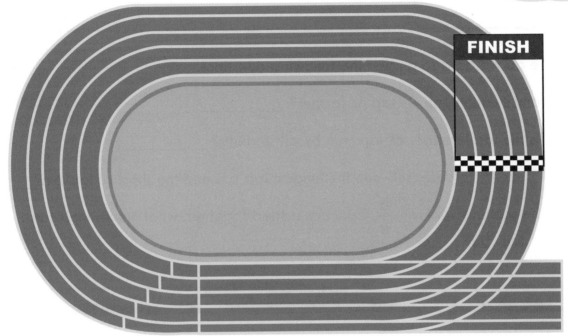

1 lap = 400 metres

Number of students	Runs around the track (in laps)
3	4/8
4	6/8
2	5/8
5	7/8
1	1/8
4	2/8

Line plot:

b. Use the above data to answer the following questions.

i. How many students ran $\frac{5}{8}$ lap or farther?_____

ii. What is the total number of laps run by all students? _____

iii. What is the difference between the longest lap run and the shortest lap run?_____

iv. If all the students who ran $\frac{6}{8}$ lap were added together, what would their total number of laps be?

_____

Weights of School Bags

Fifteen students were asked to weigh their school bags (in pounds). The weights are given below.

$$4\frac{1}{2} \quad 5\frac{3}{4} \quad 3\frac{3}{4} \quad 3\frac{1}{2} \quad 5\frac{3}{4} \quad 4\frac{3}{4} \quad 4\frac{1}{4}$$

$$5\frac{1}{4} \quad 4\frac{3}{4} \quad 5\frac{1}{4} \quad 5\frac{1}{4} \quad 4\frac{3}{4} \quad 3\frac{3}{4} \quad 3\frac{3}{4} \quad 5\frac{1}{2}$$

- Draw a line plot to display the data.

- Write a title and label the axis.

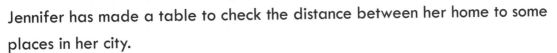

How far Is Jennifer's Home?

Jennifer has made a table to check the distance between her home to some places in her city.

Places	Shopping mall A	Shopping mall B	Museum	Theatre A	Basketball Arena A	Basketball Arena B	Theatre B
Distance (in miles)	3½	4¾	2 ¾	3¼	3½	2 ¾	4½

a. Use the information to draw a line plot. Also write title and label the axis.

b. Now use the above information to solve the problems.

i. Which place is farthest from her home?

ii. If her school is 2½ miles from her home and the museum is 2 ¾ miles from her home in a different direction, what is the distance between her school and the museum?

iii. Distance between shopping mall A and shopping mall B is 1¼ miles. If Jennifer starts from her home visits shopping mall A and from there visits shopping mall B, how much distance will she cover?

Geometric Measurement

The region between two rays starting from a common point is called an **angle.** The common point is called **vertex.** Angle represents the amount of turn between two rays, lines or line segments. An angle is commonly measured using a protractor.

Angle is the amount of rotation of one ray from the other.

The symbol used to represent an angle is '∠' and is measured in degrees (°).

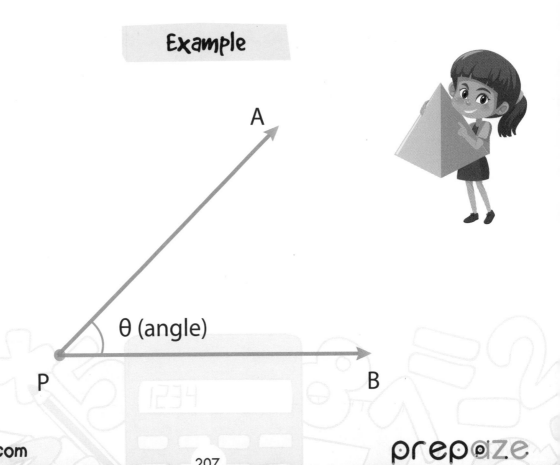

Example

θ (angle)

P

A

B

Angles are classified into various types based on their measurement.

Name of Angle	Description	Example
Acute angle	Any angle less than 90° is called an **acute angle**.	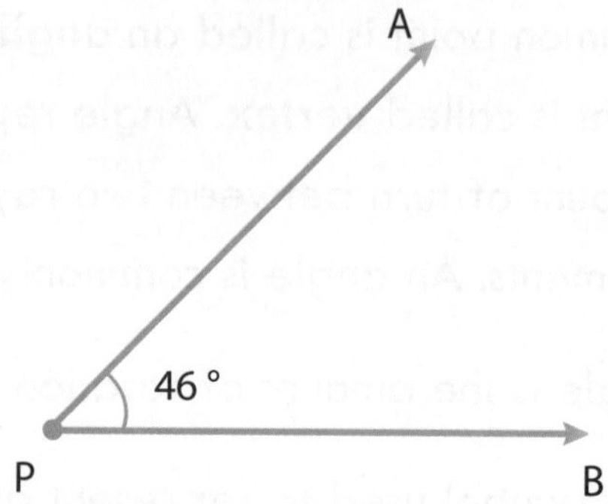
Right angle	Angle equal to 90° is called a **right angle**.	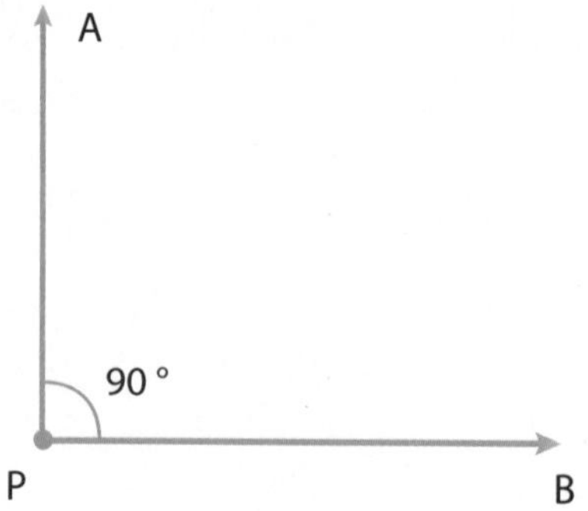
Obtuse angle	An angle that is greater than 90° and less than 180° is called an **obtuse angle**.	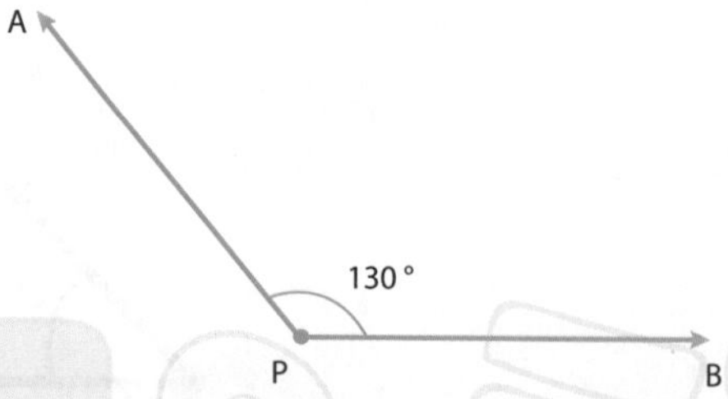

A House Full of Angles

Answer the following statements based on angles.

a. Sam added 45° to a right angle. What would be the measure of the angle now?

b. If 1° is added to an angle it becomes an obtuse angle and if 1° is subtracted from the angle it becomes an acute angle. Which angle is this?

c. What is the value of a straight angle?

d. How many 45° angles does it take to make a full turn?

e. How many right angles does it take to make a full turn?

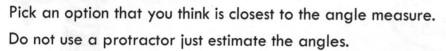

Estimate the Angle

Pick an option that you think is closest to the angle measure.
Do not use a protractor just estimate the angles.

a.

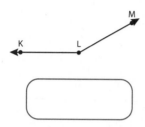

| 95 ° | 41 ° |
| 19 ° | 152 ° |

b.

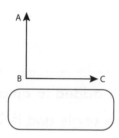

| 260 ° | 41 ° |
| 90 ° | 140 ° |

c.

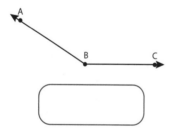

| 70 ° | 150 ° |
| 185 ° | 20 ° |

d.

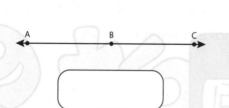

| 75 ° | 65 ° |
| 15 ° | 180 ° |

prepaze

Identify the measure of each angle.

a.

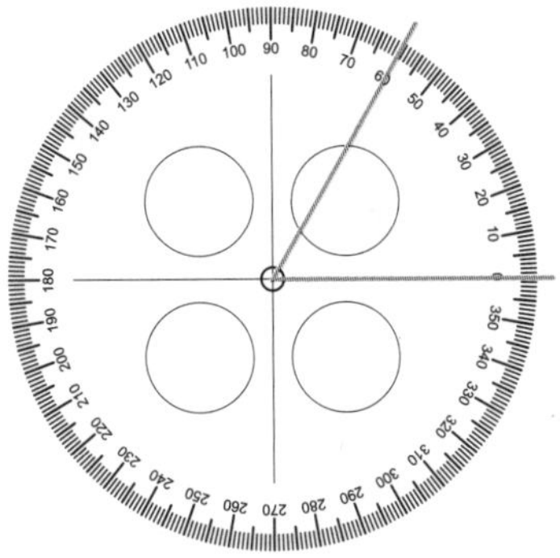

b.

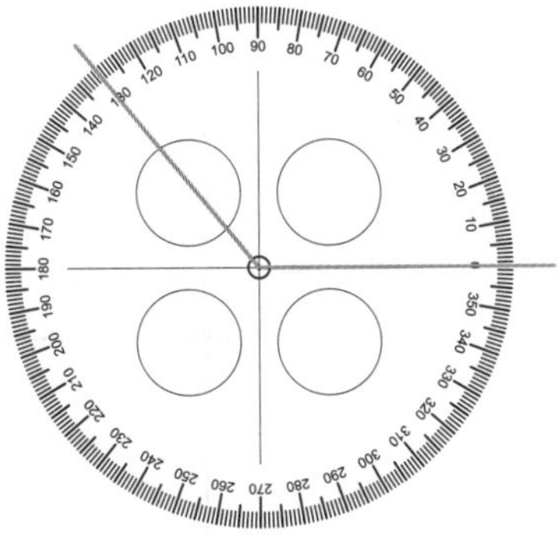

c.

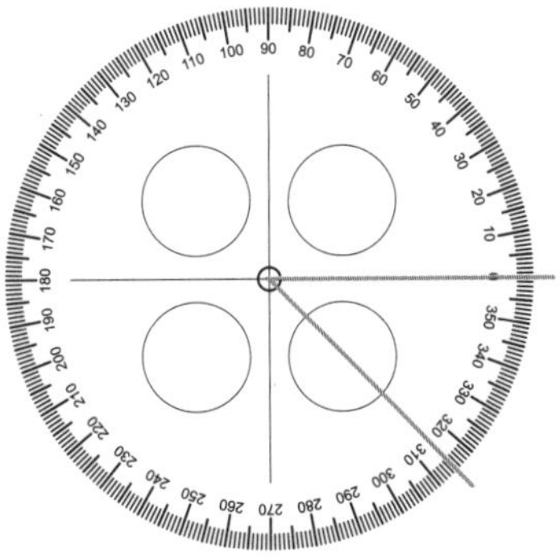

d.

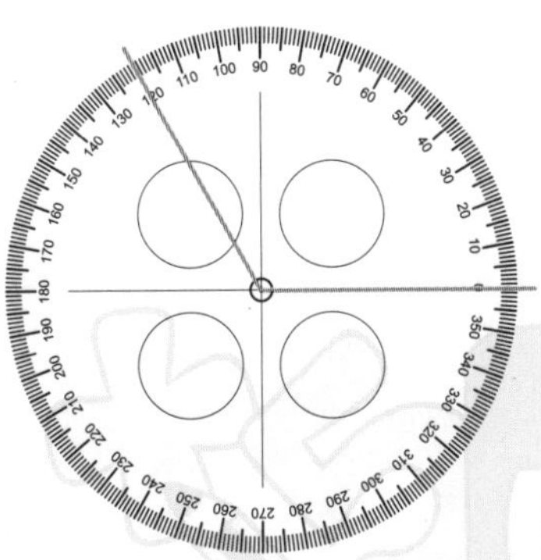

Angle Mystery

Erik and Jen measured the same angles using different sizes of circles. Erik used the red one and Jen used the green one. Did both of them get the same answer? Explain your thinking.

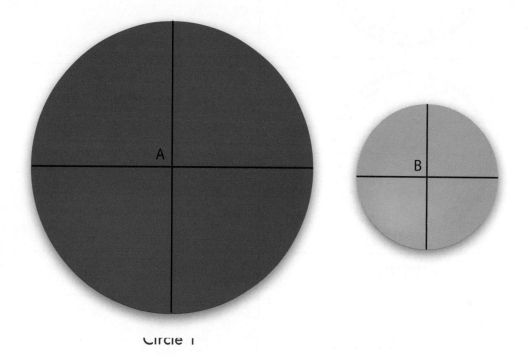

Circle 1

Find the angles between the lines of each by using a protractor.

a.

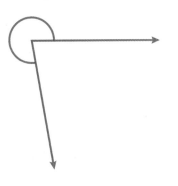

c.

d.

b.

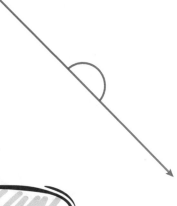

Draw Angles

Use a protractor to draw the following angles.

a. 45°

b. 270°

c. 70°

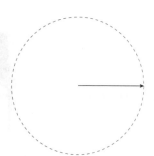

d. 150°

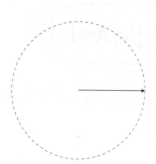

Draw the hands of a clock to show the time as given. Then, draw an arc of the angle and estimate the angle that is formed.

[Hint: Keep in mind the direction in which the hands of the clock moves]

a. 12 o'clock

Estimated Angle - _____

b. 3 o'clock

Estimated Angle - _____

c. 6 o'clock

Estimated Angle - _____

d. 9:30

Estimated Angle - _____

prepaze

Find A

Find the value of 'A'

a.

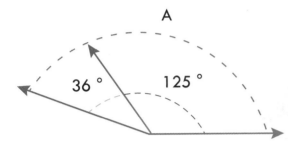

A
36 °
125 °

b.

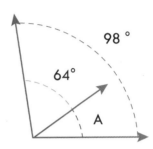

98 °
64°
A

c.

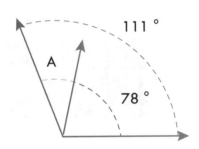

111 °
A
78 °

d.

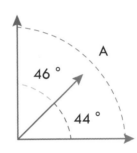

A
46 °
44 °

e.

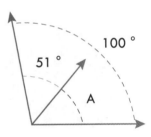

100 °
51 °
A

Without using a protractor find the angle ∠GEF.

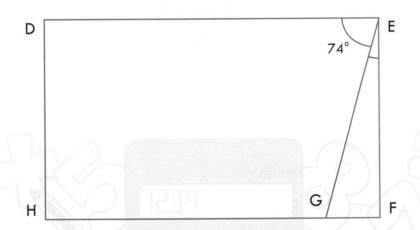

D   E
74°

H   G   F

Turn to the Right

Kristy, Hannah, and Ron stood in the middle of the road facing the house. Kristy turned 90° to the right, Hannah turned 180° to the right and Ron turned 270° to the right. What is each of them facing now?

House

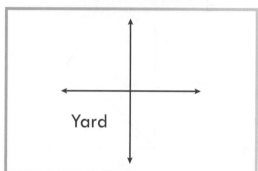

Barn

Yard

Fence

Tree

Kristy – _____

Hannah – _____

Ron – _____

prepaze

Dr. Little's 180° Degree Turn

Dr. Little drove away from this house and took a 180° degree turn near the store. Which side is he heading now?

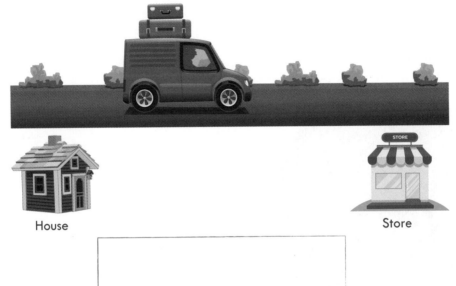

House   Store

How Many Quarter Turns Will Meredith Take?

Meredith is jogging in a circular park. How many quarter turns will she have to take in order to come back to the start position?

Square and Hexagon Problem

A hexagon is made of equal-sized triangles. Randel placed a square made up of two triangles next to the hexagon. Find the value of x.

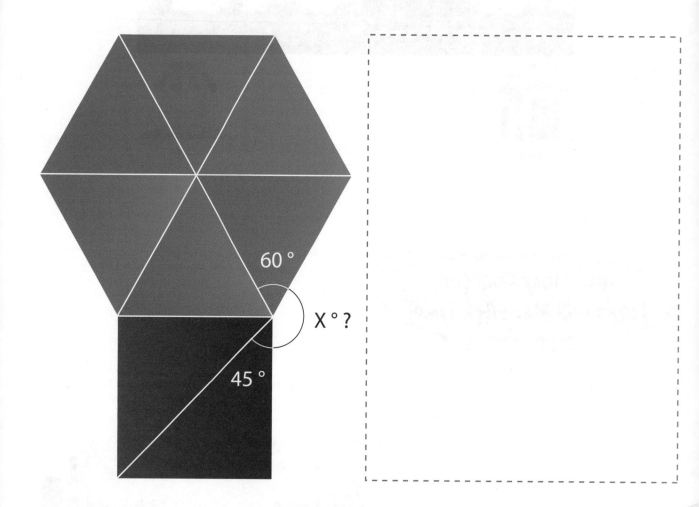

60°

X°?

45°

Henry used regular polygons to build a shape.
Calculate the angles x and z by writing addition
number statements. x° is done for you.

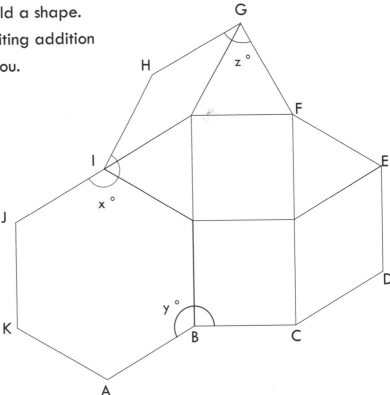

a. x° = 120° + 60° + 30°

   x° = 210°

b. y° = _____

   y° = _____

c. z° = _____

   z° = _____

Professions That Use Angles

Name two professions that use angles in their work.

Geometry

A line is one that is straight, has no thickness and extends in both directions with no end.

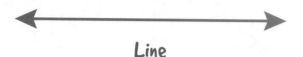

Line

A line that can extend in only one direction is called a ray.

Ray

A line that cannot extend on either sides is called a line segment.

Line Segment

Victor's Vacation

Victor is on vacation. Join his destination points using a ruler.

Mark the Arrow

Look at the arrows. Mark two acute angles, right angles, and obtuse angles.

Do I Have Perpendicular Lines?

On each object, trace at least one pair of lines that are perpendicular.

a.

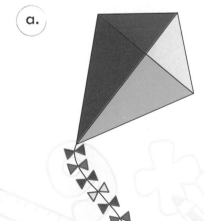

b.

c.

d.

e. How do you know if two lines are perpendicular?

_____

_____

_____

Draw a line perpendicular to the line segments given in the grid.

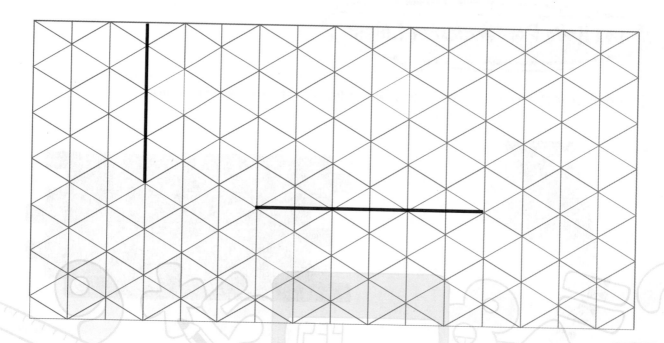

Draw a line AB such that it is perpendicular to a line CD. Label your drawing.

Parallel lines.

a. Trace at least one pair of parallel lines for each object.

b. How do you know if two lines are parallel?

c. Draw a line parallel to the given line in the grid.

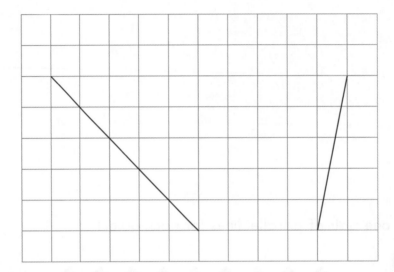

Mark a line of symmetry for each of these objects/shapes.

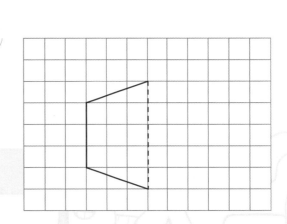

Will Zack Win the Competition?

Zack is participating in a drawing competition. Help him complete the given shapes using the line of symmetry and win the competition.

a.

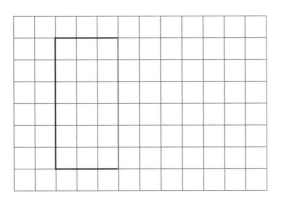

b.

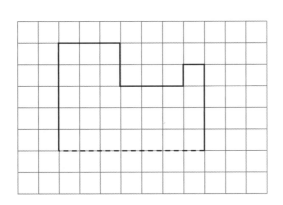

c.

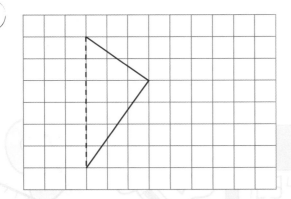

d.

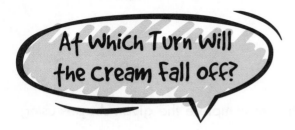

At Which Turn Will the Cream Fall Off?

If the ice cream cone is turned at a 45° angle, how many 45° angles does it take to make a full turn? Draw the position of the cone at each turn.

Lines, Angles, and Symmetry

Write your name in big bold letters and mark - lines, line segments, rays, angles, and lines of symmetry. An example is given for you. Mark at least one of each.

intersecting lines   line of symmetry   vertical line

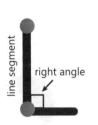    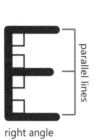 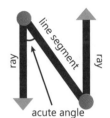

line segment   right angle   isosceles triangle   line segment   parallel lines   right angle   ray   line segment   ray   acute angle

Draw the shapes that have the following properties.

a. A right triangle

b. - 5 sides,

- at least 1 set of parallel lines

- at least one pair of perpendicular lines.

Match the words with the right picture.

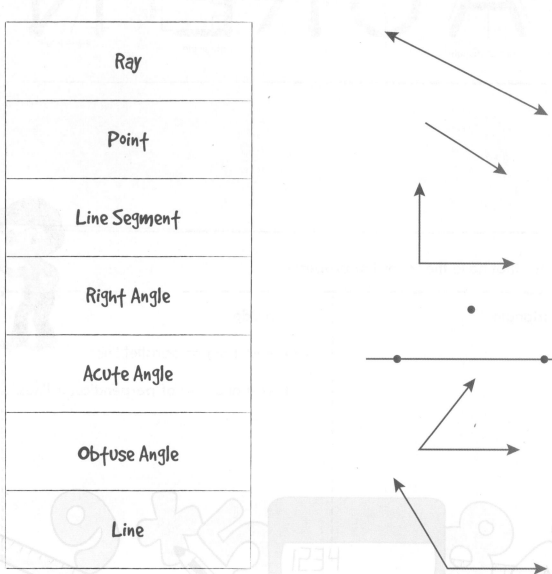

Ray
Point
Line Segment
Right Angle
Acute Angle
Obtuse Angle
Line

Science

Help your children learn and enjoy a wide range of information and fun facts that will surprise and amaze them. Find numerous Science experiments, cool facts, activities, and quizzes for the children to enjoy learning.

Physical Sciences

Everything around us is made of tiny particles that are too small to be visible to the naked eye. Each of these particles has an electrical charge. There are two kinds of electrical charge - positive and negative.

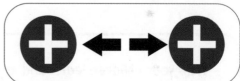

Like charges repel

- When two charges are similar, they repel (push away) each other.

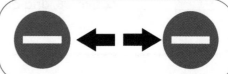

- When two charges are different, they attract (come closer) each other.

Unlike charges attract

Word Grid

Complete the following statements and find the answers in the word grid given below.

1. Like charges _____ .

2. Electrical charges flow through a single path in a _____ circuit.

3. An electrical apparatus that can increase or decrease the voltage in an electric circuit is a _____ .

4. A _____ melts to open a circuit if the electrical current gets too high.

5. Electrical charges flow through more than one path in a _____ circuit.

6. After you walk on a woolen carpet and touch a metal door knob you will receive an electrical shock. This is because the metal in the door knob is a _____ .

7. Rubber is an _____ which does not allow electric charges to flow through it.

8. A positive charge and a negative charge _____ each other.

9. The electric force that causes the movement of free electrons is called _____ .

10. The discharge of static electricity between clouds is called _____ .

11. A light bulb in a circuit is the _____ .

s	u	p	e	r	m	a	c	h	i	o	p	e	n	t	c
h	h	e	t	r	a	n	s	f	o	r	m	e	r	b	o
o	t	t	p	a	r	a	l	l	e	l	l	e	x	s	n
g	i	o	y	y	a	k	i	a	a	f	i	i	e	e	d
s	n	a	g	o	o	d	g	p	a	u	z	i	h	r	u
a	s	m	e	n	n	v	h	o	p	s	r	o	d	a	c
a	u	k	a	v	o	l	t	a	g	e	e	d	h	t	t
n	l	a	g	e	s	h	n	o	s	i	p	n	k	t	o
s	a	t	e	v	w	o	i	n	d	r	e	f	u	r	r
l	t	o	l	l	u	s	n	a	b	h	l	a	m	a	n
o	o	l	o	a	d	h	g	r	s	o	i	n	g	c	y
r	r	e	i	g	n	y	d	a	a	w	w	e	n	t	l

Race Your Can without Touching It

Let's explore static electricity with an activity.

What you need:

- 2 balloons
- 2 empty soda cans
- Sticky tape
- A table or smooth surface
- Measuring tape

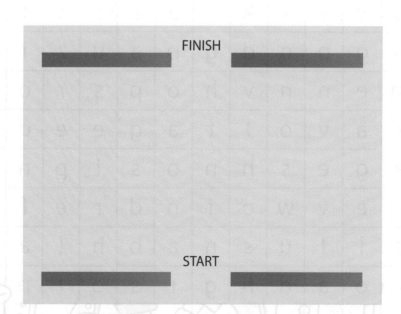

prepaze

Prior preparation

Remove the label on the soda cans with the help of an adult. Ensure that the soda cans are not crushed or dented and can easily roll on a surface.

What to do:

 Have a friend to play this with. Take one balloon each.

 Both of you blow the balloons into their full sizes and knot the end of the balloon.

 On the smooth surface, measure one meter. Mark one end as the 'START' point and the other end as the 'FINISH' point.

 Place your can horizontally along the start line.

 Rub the balloon on your hair vigorously and place the balloon close to the can. Do not touch the can with the balloon.

 Ensure that the surface of the balloon that you rubbed on the hair faces the can. Notice that the can starts moving.

 Keep repeating this until the can reaches the 'FINISH' line.

prepaze

Observation

1. How did the balloon affect the can?

☐   The can stayed still.

☐   The can moved closer to the balloon.

☐   The can moved away from the balloon.

2. How will you describe the movement of the balloon and the can?

☐   Attraction

☐   Repulsion

3. The can has a lot of negative charges on its surface. What charges do you think were more on the surface of the balloon after you rubbed it on your hair?

☐   Positive charges

☐   Negative charges

☐   Neutral

Inference

The can _____ (moved away from/moved towards) the balloon due to

_____ (repulsion/attraction) between _____ (like/opposite)

charges. This movement is caused due to _____ .

prepaze

Static Electricity

Find which of the following balloons will attract, repel, or remain still.
Write the reason below.

1.

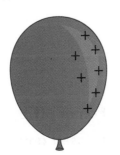

Reason:

_____

_____

2.

Reason:

_____

_____

3.

 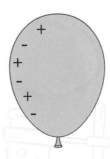

Reason:

_____

_____

prepaze

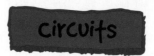
The closed path in which the electric charges flow is called a circuit. A circuit includes several parts such as:

- a power source

- wires and

- the load (Example: bulbs, television, computer).

Some circuits may have a switch. This turns the current on or off by opening or closing the circuit. When the switch in a circuit is ON, the circuit is closed and electric current will flow through it. This is a closed circuit.

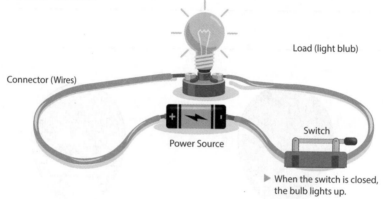

Load (light blub)

Connector (Wires)

Power Source

Switch

▶ When the switch is closed, the bulb lights up.

When the switch in a circuit is OFF, the current cannot flow through it. This is an open circuit.

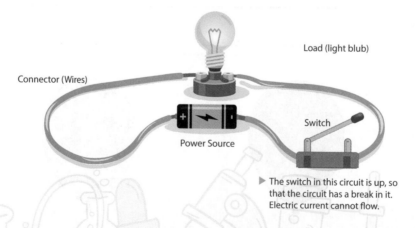

Load (light blub)

Connector (Wires)

Power Source

Switch

▶ The switch in this circuit is up, so that the circuit has a break in it. Electric current cannot flow.

Electrical energy can be converted into other usable forms such as heat, light, and motion. These energy conversions are majorly used in burners, light bulbs, and cars.

Connecting Circuits

Battery 1

Bulb A

Bulb B

Bulb C

Battery 2

What you need:

 Marker pens - green and red

1. Circuit 1

Using a green marker, draw wires and make a closed circuit to make Bulb A glow using Battery.

1. Draw arrows along the wires to indicate the direction of flow of electric charges in the circuit.

a. What is the name of the circuit you just made?

2. Circuit 2

Using a red marker, draw wires and make a parallel circuit to make Bulb B and Bulb C glow using Battery

2. Draw arrows along the wires to indicate the direction of flow of electric charges in the circuit.

a. Will Bulb B still glow if Bulb C burns out? Why?

☐   Yes

☐   No

3. What will you add to the circuit to turn on and off the bulbs instead of removing the wires?

_____

_____

4. Draw your own circuit with parts of your choice in the space below and label them.

DIY Night Lamp

What you need:

- 3 mini light bulbs
- 2 D - batteries
- Connecting wires fitted with crocodile clips at the ends
- 2 battery holders
- 3 mini bulb holders
- Switch

- Clear color wrap sheets (your choice of color)
- Glue
- A pair of scissors
- 8 popsicle sticks
- 4 paper straws (the ones used to drink bubble tea)

Connecting wires with crocodile clips fitted at the ends

Battery holder

Switch

Mini bulb holder

Mini bulbs

Battery

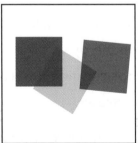

Clear Color Wrap sheets

What to do:

 **Make the lamp shade**

1. Take 4 popsicle sticks and use glue to stick them end to end. Form a square as shown in the image.

Repeat and make another square.

2. Take one paper straw and compare the length of the straw with one side of the colored wrap sheet. Ensure that they are of the same length; if not, cut either the straw or the wrap sheet to match their lengths.

Have five such sheets ready.

3. Take one square and apply glue in four corners.

Next, take the four paper straws. Apply glue to one end of each straw. Stick one straw in each of the corners of the square.

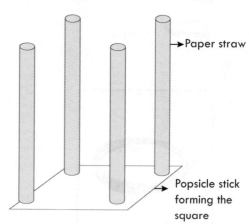

Paper straw

Popsicle stick forming the square

4. Take the second square made of popsicle sticks and apply glue on four corners. Apply some glue on the open ends of the paper straws. Stick the popsicle stick square with glue side over the paper straws.

The final structure will look as shown in the image.

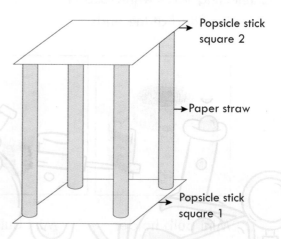

Popsicle stick square 2

Paper straw

Popsicle stick square 1

5. Leave the setup to dry for 30 minutes.

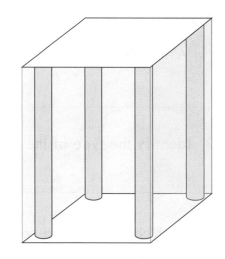

6. Next, apply glue on all the four paper straws in the structure. Then, stick colored wrap sheets on the straws. The final structure will have all four sides covered.

7. Now, on one end apply glue on the popsicle stick square and stick a wrap sheet flat on top. Leave the setup to dry. The lamp shade that you make will look similar to the image shown.

 **Make the circuit**

1. Fit the battery in the battery holder and two bulbs in two bulb holders.

2. Using the switch, battery, bulbs, and the connecting wires make a circuit. (Take the help of an adult to connect wires, if necessary). Ensure that the switch is open while making the circuit.

3. Use any of the following circuits to help you create the circuit.

4. Once the circuit is made, close the switch and place the dried lampshade on top of the circuit. Your night lamp is ready.

Answer the following questions.

1. Which circuit did you use?

_____

2. Identify the type of the circuit you used.

_____

3. In which circuit would you be able to control the brightness of the lamp without breaking the circuit? Why?

_____

4. Explain how you will do it.

_____

_____

_____

_____

_____

_____

_____

_____

Electrical Energy in other Useful Forms

a. Can electrical energy be transformed to other useful forms?

_____

b. Find the odd one from the following.

1.

| heat | energy | train | lamp |

2.

| energy | motion | bulb | light |

3.

| car | train | burner | washing machine |

4.

| electric kettle | burner | dryers | fan |

5.

| torch | bulb | night lamp | toaster |

Magnets are objects that attract certain metal objects. A magnet can repel or attract any other magnet. Any magnet has two magnetic poles - north (N) pole and south (S) pole.

A pole of a magnet is a part where its ability to push or pull another magnet is the strongest.

When two magnets are brought closer to each other, opposite poles attract and like poles repel, similar to electric charges..

Make Your own Compass

What you need:

- A needle
- A cork/1-inch thermocol
- A small glass bowl
- Water
- A magnet
- A pair of scissors

What to do:

Note: Do the following activity during the day when the Sun is out. This gives you the direction East (or) ask adults in which direction (or side of your house/school) did the sun rise that day. You will know the importance of this later in the activity.

 Hold the needle by its blunt end and rub the sharp end on the magnet.

 Ensure that you rub the needle in only one direction, that is, stroke the needle from left to right or left to right. Once you reach the other end, lift the needle to return to the starting position.

 Repeat 40 times.

 Cut the cork or thermocol in the size of a coin.

 Insert the needle through the cork or thermocol as shown.

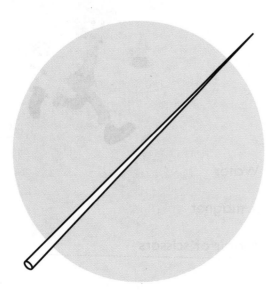

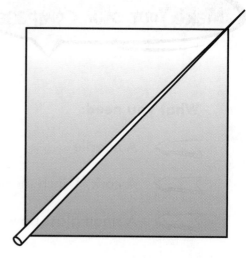

 Step 6   Fill the glass bowl with some water.

 Step 7   Let the cork and needle (or the thermocol and needle) float on the water and set it on the floor.

 Step 8   The cork or thermocol with the needle will slowly turn either clockwise or counter-clockwise and align itself in the north-south direction along the Earth's magnetic field.

 Step 9   If there is no movement, rub the needle again on the magnet and set it up again.

 Step 10   Use the direction from which the sun rose in your house and image below and find North and verify the correctness of the compass you just made.

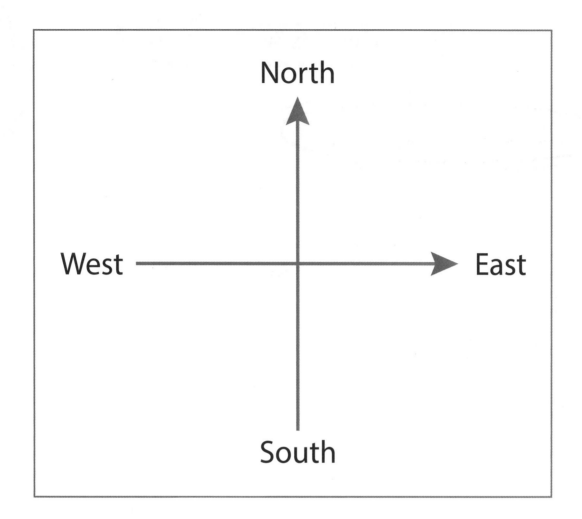

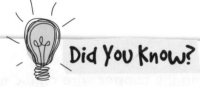 Did You Know?

An electromagnet is a magnet made when an electric current flows through a coil of wire wrapped around an iron rod. When the current flows through the coil, the iron rod acts like a magnet. Its two ends become the north pole and south pole.

Electromagnets have a wide range of uses such as in doorbells, toy cars and trains, loudspeakers, telephones, and so on.

Electromagnets and Their Uses

Make Your Own Electromagnet

What you need:

- A battery
- Thin copper wire (30 cm)
- A iron nail or screen (about 2 inches long)
- Sticky tape
- Sand paper

- A pair of scissors
- Metal paper clips (few)
- Safety pins (few)
- Metal springs (few)
- A small plastic box

What to do:

1. Take the copper wire and the iron nail.

2. Leave 3 inches at the end of the wire and start winding the copper wire on the nail.

3. Ensure that the windings are placed close to each other and tight on the nail. Refer to the given image.

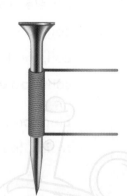

4. Try to wind as many windings as possible close to each other.

5. Once that is done, leave 3 inches of the wire at the end.

6. On both the free ends of the wire remove the insulation by rubbing the sandpaper on the wire. On removal of the insulation, the wire will look silver in color.

7. Make a small coil at both the ends.

8. Cut two pieces of sticky tape and have them ready.

9. Attach each end of the copper wire (coiled part) to each end of the battery. Stick the wire to the battery using sticky tape.

10. Your electromagnet is ready.

11. Place a few paper clips, safety pins, springs on the table and move the electromagnet close to these objects. Record your observations.

Observation

- Does your electromagnet attract the items on the tables?   Yes / No

- If yes, you have made an electromagnet. Place this setup inside a small plastic box. Now try moving this box over the metal clips. Does it still attract them?   Yes / No

- Why do you think this happens?

_____

_____

_____

Note: If you feel the battery is getting heated up, disconnect the wires and allow it to cool for a while.

How do Doorbells Work?

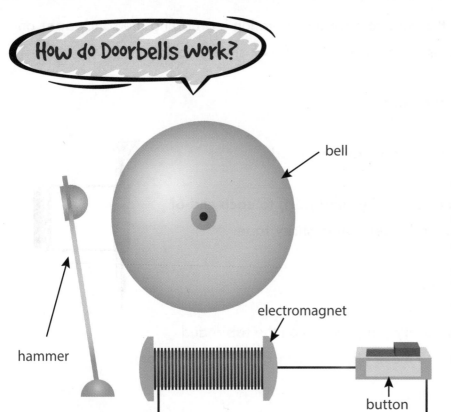

bell

electromagnet

hammer

button

The image given here shows the electromagnet in the circuit of a door bell.

Observe the image and answer the questions that follow.

1. When will the electromagnet attract the metallic hammer to hit the bell? Why?

_____

_____

_____

2. Can you use a magnet instead of an electromagnet?

_____

3. How will the function of the doorbell change if a magnet is used?

_____

_____

prepaze

Electromagnets in Phones, Electric Motor, and Generator

Number the following sets of statements in the correct order.

A. How does the electromagnet function in a telephone - from the dialler to the receiver?

☐ The electromagnet in the receiver on your phone converts the electrical signals into sound.

☐ The microphone in the mouthpiece of the phone has a magnet. It converts sound to electrical signals.

☐ The receiver hears the sound.

☐ The electrical signals travel to the receiver.

☐ The speaker speaks into the mouthpiece.

B. How does an electromagnet function in an electric motor fitted in a toy car?

☐ The permanent magnet pushes and pulls the wire loop making it spin.

☐ The shaft, in turn, spins a wheel.

☐ The electrical current from the battery runs through the wire loop making a magnetic field around the wire loop.

☐ The toy car moves.

☐ The spinning wire loop spins the shaft.

C. How does an electromagnet function in a generator to produce electrical energy?

☐ The turbine connected to a wire loop turns between the poles of a magnet.

☐ As a result, the magnet is surrounded by a magnetic field.

☐ Water spins the turbine.

☐ Current flows through the wire loop as the loop moves through the magnetic field there by generating electrical energy.

prepaze

Life Sciences

Plants

Photosynthesis Word Grid

Complete the following statements and find the answers in the word grid.

1. Plants trap sunlight through the _____ present in the leaves.

2. Plants make their own food and give out_____ .

3. _____ allow the gas carbon dioxide to enter the leaves.

4. Plants make their own food by_____ .

5. The_____ take water to the stem.

6. The stem takes water to the_____ .

7. _____ , water, and carbon dioxide are required by plants to make their own food.

p	v	a	a	d	i	a	m	m	a	j	k	k	m
a	h	m	o	c	f	s	u	n	l	i	g	h	t
s	r	o	e	h	e	r	a	g	a	m	o	k	e
m	u	l	t	l	i	z	l	e	a	v	e	s	u
o	o	t	y	o	g	o	o	d	s	v	a	n	d
s	o	l	i	r	s	t	h	a	v	a	k	l	i
m	u	j	e	o	x	y	g	e	n	k	e	h	n
a	v	r	a	p	k	a	n	c	h	e	k	c	h
z	u	b	i	h	n	m	s	t	o	m	a	t	a
i	r	a	n	y	n	i	k	a	h	a	n	i	p
v	b	l	n	l	b	i	o	t	r	e	r	o	b
o	t	e	m	l	e	d	i	o	n	g	s	o	x
o	r	o	o	t	s	t	h	i	k	i	n	i	u
j	i	t	h	u	j	i	l	a	d	i	n	i	s

Process of Photosynthesis

Complete the following table.

Photosynthesis needs:	Photosynthesis produces:
1. _____	1. _____
2. _____	2. _____
3. _____	
Parts of a leaf that help in photosynthesis:	
1. _____	
2. _____	

Observe the picture given below and answer the questions.

1. Which plant do you think will make its own food? Why?

_____

_____

_____

2. Draw and describe how plants make their own food.

_____

_____

_____

3. How do you think Plant B gets energy?

_____

_____

_____

Food Chains Around You

Ryan has a vegetable garden. In the garden, there are bees sucking nectar from flowers and birds pecking seeds from the ground. Hannah harvests her daily dose of greens from her own garden.

1. Identify the producers and consumers from the above scenario and list them in the table below.

Producers	Consumers

2. List three other producers and consumers from your surroundings.

Producers	Consumers

prepaze

3. Write or draw one simple food chain that you observe around you.

food Chain and food web

A **food chain** is the path energy takes in the form of food from one organism to another. All food chains start with energy from the Sun, which is then used by plants to make food.

Plant is the **producer** in a food chain since it makes food. Any insect that consumes the plant becomes the first **consumer** in the food chain. Consumers cannot make food of their own and hence feed on producers and other consumers for energy. A frog that eats the insect in a food chain becomes the next consumer and so on. The chain continues until the consumers die.

Many food chains happen simultaneously. Such food chains, when they interlink form a **food web** in that environment. Food webs give us a clear idea of how certain living things depend on more than one living thing for energy.

Food chains and food webs continue until the consumers die. The dead consumers are then broken down by **decomposers** like earthworm, beetles, and flies.

create a food chain

Observe the given images and answer the questions that follow.

1. How many food chains do you see?

Write the food chain as shown in the template below.

(Hint: To make a food chain you need to connect at least three living things that depend on other organisms for food)

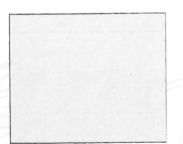  

2. What is a food web?

_____

_____

3. Can the organisms in the pictures given above form a food web?

☐   Yes

☐   No

4. Draw a food web with these organisms and label it. (Write the names of the living things to make the food web. Drawing the living things is optional).

5. Which among the given living things is the following?

Herbivore: _____

Carnivore: _____

Omnivore: _____

Given above are producers and some consumers that form some food chains and a food web.

1. How many food chains can you find interlinked in the given food web?

_____

_____

2. Write the food chains below. Use the names of the living things to write the food chains.

3. How will the food web change if there were no frogs?

a. Mention the living things that will be in excess.

_____

b. Mention the living things that will be left with less or no food.

_____

c. Explain your answer.

_____

_____

_____

prepaze

Food Webs around You

1. Draw a food web with at least three food chains interlinked that you observe in your surroundings.

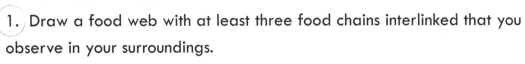

2. a. Where will you place the decomposers such as bacteria in your food web? Why?

_____

b. Are decomposers producers or consumers? Give reasons for your answer and an example.

_____

_____

Ecosystem

An **ecosystem** is an area where all living things and nonliving things interact and work together. Living things include plants, insects, animals, and microorganisms. The non-living things in an ecosystem include sunlight, air, water, and soil. Climatic conditions of a region also play a major role in the ecosystem.

Ecosystems can be of different types such as:

- desert ecosystem

- coral-reef ecosystem

- pond ecosystem

- rainforest ecosystem

Plants and animals living in each of these ecosystems depend on each other and on the non-living things to thrive.

Plants and animals develop many **adaptations** to live in their ecosystems. For example, plants like cactus have adaptations to retain water and roots to absorb water quickly in deserts. Animals living in colder regions such as the Arctic have adaptations such as fur and a thick layer of fat under their skin to keep them warm.

Ecosystem and Its Components

In a pond ecosystem,

- plants grow by the edge using the water and nourishment from the soil,

- water birds build their nests by the bank in the plants,

- insects feed on the plants that grow,

- frogs feed on the insects,

- fish feed on small worms and water plants,

- Birds feed on small fish in the pond.

1. What are the living and nonliving things in this ecosystem?

Living things	Nonliving things

2. How will this ecosystem change if the pond dried up?

a. Describe how each living thing will get affected.

Plants - _____

Birds - _____

Worms - _____

Fish - _____

Frog - _____

Insects - _____

b. Mention one way in which this pond ecosystem can go back to normal.

_____

_____

_____

prepaze

Desert Ecosystem

1. Mention three characteristics of a desert region.

_____

_____

_____

_____

2. Camel is a desert animal. Research on it and write three adaptations that it has to survive in the desert ecosystem.

_____

_____

_____

_____

_____

_____

3. If you were to live in the desert, write three adaptations that you should have.

_____

_____

_____

_____

Imagine you live in a treehouse built just below the tree tops. It is hot and rainy with lots of trees around.

1. Can you identify the ecosystem in which you are living?

_____

2. Which part of the ecosystem is your treehouse located. Choose from the options below:

a. Forest floor

b. Emergent layer

c. Canopy

d. Understory

3. Name 5 living things you are likely to see from your treehouse.

_____

_____

4. Mention the nonliving things that support life in this ecosystem.

_____

_____

_____

_____

_____

5. Explain how the living things are dependent on the nonliving things?

_____

_____

_____

_____

_____

_____

_____

Interdependence of organisms

Plants and animals depend on each other. Plants make their own food and become food for herbivorous animals. They also serve as shelter for a wide range of animals like snakes, birds, monkeys, and leopards.

Plants depend on animals to continue living and to reproduce too. Insects such as bees, flies, and birds such as hummingbirds help plants in pollination. Pollination is a process where pollen from the stamen of a flower are transferred to the pistil of another flower. Seeds are made in the pistil from which new plants grow.

Animals also help plants in carrying these seeds to different places where new plants can grow from these seeds.

prepaze

Observe the images and complete the table.

Plants and animals that are dependent on each other	How is the plant dependent on the animal?	How is the animal dependent on the plant?
Bee sitting on a flower		
Bird eating papaya fruit and seeds		
Squirrel eating nut on a tree		

Changes in the Ecosystem

Answer the following questions.

1. Three human activities that change an ecosystem.

   a. _____

   b. _____

   c. _____

2. Three natural events that can change an ecosystem.

   a. _____

   b. _____

   c. _____

3. How can you help in the following scenarios that cause a change in the ecosystem?

Scenario	What can you do?
Fishes and turtles in the sea get trapped in plastic bags and wires and die. The plastic bags and wires do not naturally occur in the sea. They are washed away from the beaches that we visit.	
Some birds have become endangered due to humans cutting down trees and constructing buildings. Soon these birds will become extinct.	
Human beings use vehicles such as cars and motorbikes to travel short distances. This gives out smoke and makes the air hard to breathe for all living things.	

Observe the images and answer the question that follows.

Spot the butterfly.

It adapts itself to look like a leaf and avoid being eaten by other animals.

What is the name of this adaptation?

_____

Spot the owl.

The owl blends itself into the bark of the tree so that it cannot be seen.

Name this adaptation.

_____

Aloe vera is a desert plant which has small roots that absorb water quickly. It has fleshy leaves and small spines which prevents animals from eating it.

Mention the purpose for these adaptations.

_____

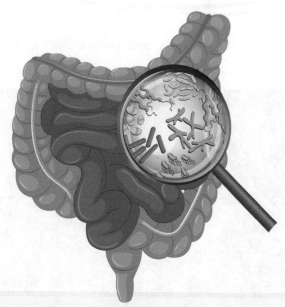

1. Explain how mold found in stale bread is different from bacteria in your stomach.

_____

_____

_____

_____

2. Find out and write the names of 3 more microorganisms that are harmful and useful to humans.

Useful microorganisms	Harmful microorganisms

Earth Sciences

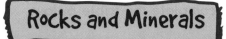

Rocks and Minerals

Rocks are solid materials found above and below the Earth's surface. Rocks are found in molten form called **magma** inside the Earth. This magma comes out as lava through volcanic eruptions and forms what is called the **igneous rocks.**

Some other types of rocks are formed over years of deposition of sediments that wind and water carry. These are called **sedimentary rocks.** There are rocks which are formed when they are constantly pressed against each other with heat. Such rocks are called **metamorphic rocks.**

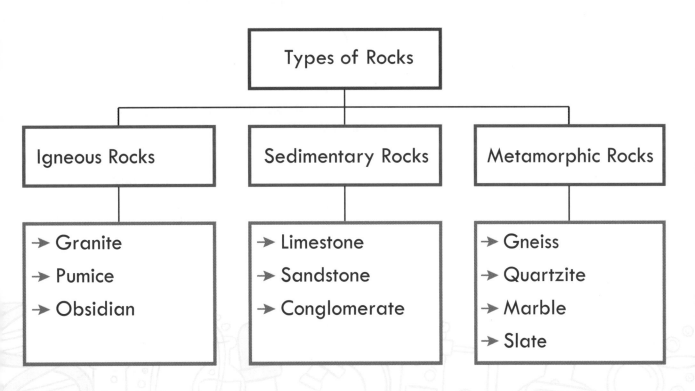

Types of Rocks

Igneous Rocks	Sedimentary Rocks	Metamorphic Rocks
→ Granite → Pumice → Obsidian	→ Limestone → Sandstone → Conglomerate	→ Gneiss → Quartzite → Marble → Slate

Given below are properties of three different types of rock. Identify the name of the rock and group the properties to complete the table below.

- Formed from bits of sand cemented together
- Very light in weight
- Formed from granite
- Sand is made of the mineral quartz
- Has layers across the rock
- May show ripples if it was formed under water
- Formed above the ground
- Has minerals that are large enough to be seen
- Feel crumbly, scratchy

Properties	Name of Rock	Type of Rock
		Igneous
	Sandstone	
Formed from granite		Metamorphic

Uses of Rocks

Given here are some properties, uses of some rock. Identify the name and type of rock, group the properties, and complete the table below.

- Formed at the bottom of the oceans

- Does not have layers

- Formed from sandstone

- Has small mineral and feels smooth

- Often has fossils

- Can be used to make roof tiles

- Can be used for making glass and pottery

- Has small minerals inside

- Formed from shale

- Formed from bones and shells

- Can be used to make chalk

Properties	Uses of the rock	Name of the rock	Type of rock
Formed at the bottom of the ceans			Sedimentary
	Can be used for making glass and pottery		
		Slate	

prepaze

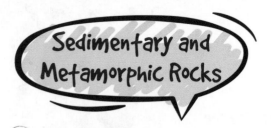

Sedimentary and Metamorphic Rocks

A. Match the metamorphic rocks on the right with the sedimentary and igneous rocks on the left from which they are formed.

(Hint: Recall how the rocks on the right are formed)

1	soft coal	slate
2	limestone	schist
3	granite	quartzite
4	slate	marble
5	sandstone	hard coal
6	shale	gneiss

B. Number the following sentences in the correct order.

- _____ There are many kinds of sedimentary rocks. Many contain fossils.

- _____ The sediment in the lower layers are cemented together and become sedimentary rocks.

- _____ The moving things drop off sediments and layers form.

- _____ Layers build up, one on top of the other.

- _____ Moving things such as wind, rivers, and streams pick up and carry sediments.

- _____ Some examples are limestone, sandstone, and conglomerate.

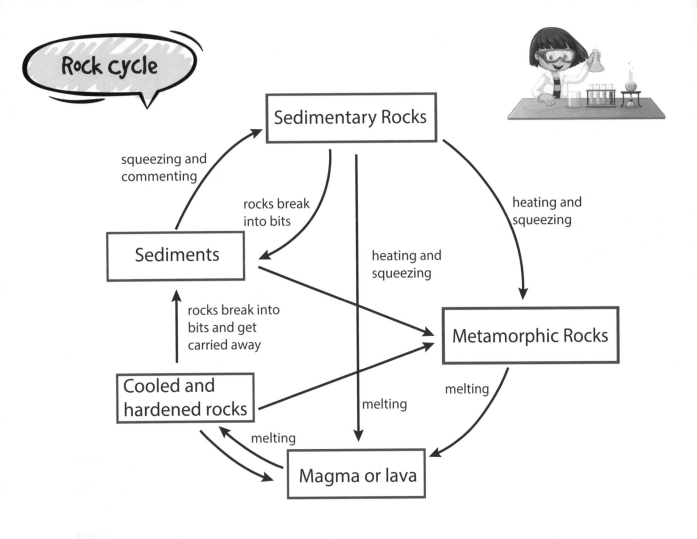

Rock cycle

Sedimentary Rocks

squeezing and commenting

rocks break into bits

heating and squeezing

Sediments

heating and squeezing

rocks break into bits and get carried away

Metamorphic Rocks

Cooled and hardened rocks

melting

melting

melting

melting

Magma or lava

Read the rock cycle given here. There are three arrows pointing out from sedimentary rocks. Read the read text near those arrows and answer the following.

What are the three things that can happen to a sedimentary rock?

_____

_____

_____

_____

_____

_____

_____

prepaze

Minerals

Minerals are parts that make the rocks. Different types of rocks contain different types of minerals. Each of these have specific properties which can be used to differentiate the minerals for different uses.

Complete the crossword.

Across

4. ability of one mineral to scratch another mineral

7. parts that rocks are made of

10. pink mineral found in granite

12. white or colorless mineral

Down

1. electric wires and pots are made out of this

2. comes from the ore bauxite

3. rocks that contain useful minerals

5. color observed when a mineral is scratched

6. mineral that splits into flakes

8. it is the way something shines in the light

9. yellow mineral also called fool's gold

11. mineral with the highest hardness number

Identifying Minerals

John and Rio went on a hike. They both found a small piece of rock each which had the following properties:

John's rock	Rio's rock
• The rock broke while streaking • Glass like luster, no shine • It could scratch feldspar but not quartz • Color - black • Breaks unevenly	• Leaves a white streak • Glass like luster, no shine • It could not scratch quartz • Color - pink • Breaks evenly

Given here is a mineral identification chart and a hardness scale. Using these, find out what John's and Rio's rocks are made of.

Mineral	Hardness	Luster	Streak	Color	Splits
Quartz	7	No shine	none	Colorless, white, pink, purple	Breaks unevenly
Mica	2 - 2.5	nonmetallic	none	Dark brown, black or silver white	flakes
Feldspar	6 - 6.5	No shine	White	White, pink, grey, black brown	Breaks evenly
Calcite	3	nonmetallic	white	colorless, white	Boxlike shapes
Hornblende	?	No shine	Colorless, Breaks leaving dust behind	Black, dark green or dark brown	Breaks unevenly

Hardness scale:

1	Talc
2	Gypsum
3	Calcite
4	Fluorite
5	Apatite
6	Feldspar
7	Quartz
8	Topaz
9	Corundum
10	Diamond

Answer the following questions.

1. John's rock has the mineral_____.

2. Rio's rock has the mineral _____.

3. Hardness of John's rock can be _____.

4. Why?_____

5. Can the mineral in John's rock scratch the one in Rio's rock?   Yes / No

Why?_____

prepaze

Processes that Change Landforms

Several natural events occur around us that change the landforms on the Earth's surface. Landforms include the following:

Mountains, the tallest landforms

Hills, land rising above the surface but not as tall as mountains

Plains, wide, flat stretches of land without any hills or mountains

Winding rivers

Beaches

Deserts

These landforms are subject to continuous change, either slow or fast.

Landform changing processes

Slow processes

- Physical weathering such as freezing and melting, splitting of rocks due to plants, wind, peeling

- Chemical weathering due to oxygen and water, carbon dioxide and water which form acids and erode rocks

- Moving water such as rivers from mountain tops which cut canyons, valley on landforms over years

- Moving glaciers which break down rocks and carry with them

Fast processes

- Landslides caused by loose soil

- Floods, flowing water that washes soil and rocks away

- Mudslides caused by water logged soil after floods

- Earthquakes that are caused due to the movement of the plate on the Earth's crust

- Tsunamis, caused by earthquakes in the ocean

- Volcanic eruptions caused when molten magma comes out to the Earth's surface with force

prepaze

Changes in Landforms

Use the words in the box below to describe each of the following sentences.

1. Wind and rain hit on rocks to break them down into smaller pieces.

   _____

2. Water seeps into cracks in the rocks, freezes forming ice. This widens the crack and breaks down rocks.

   _____

3. When wind and water carrying rock pieces are slowed down, they drop off the pieces.

   _____

4. Carbon dioxide in the air mixes with rain to form acids. Acids seep into the soil and eat away holes in rocks.

   _____

5. An area formed near the mouth of the ocean formed by deposits of a river.

   _____

6. Over time, soil forms layers due to weathering.

   _____

7. Mountain streams form rivers which over time, flow downhill and form these.

   _____

8. Thick large ice sheets flowing downhill picking up and breaking down rocks.

   _____

9. A deep narrow landform which often has rivers at the bottom.

   _____

10. Dead plants and animals rot and form a layer in soil.

    _____

Delta	Freezing and melting	Canyon	Chemical weathering	Deposition
Horizons	glacier	Humus	Physical weathering	Valley

prepaze

Journey of a Snow Particle

Imagine you are a particle of snow on top of a mountain. Draw and describe the changes that you will go through and the things you will do on your way down - in the mountain, in the river and at the ocean.

Layers of Soil

1. How is soil formed?

_____

_____

_____

2. What are the different layers of soil that are formed? Name and describe each of them in the image below.

George and Martha own a farm on a hill. They have planted coffee seeds which have grown into small plants. One day there were strong winds and heavy rains. George and Martha found that the small plants on their farm were all gone.

1. What could have happened to the plants? Name the process.

_____

_____

2. Write two things that George and Martha can do on their farm to protect and grow their coffee plants. Explain how your suggestions will help them farm.

Things that George and Martha can do on the farm	Effects

Slow and Fast Changes

Earth's crust is broken at many places forming plates. These plates often move and rub against each other.

Complete the table below.

	Name of the effect	Damages that occur	Two ways we can save ourselves from it
Effects of movement of plates on land			
Effects of movement of plates inside water (ocean)			

Volcanoes

1. Color and mark the different parts of a volcano using the words inside the box.

vent	crater	magma	lava	ash

2. Volcanoes erupt and the lava cools off around the crater in the shape of a mountain over time. What type of rocks can you find in this mountain? Give an example.

_____

_____

_____

_____

 Did You Know?

Volcanoes are not only present on land, they are also found underwater deep in the ocean. These are called **submarine volcanoes.**

The magma from these volcanoes flows on to the sea bed, cools down to form rocks. The volcanic mountains that form in the deep ocean are called **seamounts.**

Processes that Change Landforms

Landforms on the Earth undergo continuous change due to natural events. Choose any two processes that change landforms slowly and two processes that change the landforms fast and differentiate between them.

Processes that change landforms slowly	
Name of the process:	Name of the process:

prepaze

Processes that change landforms fast	
Name of the process:	Name of the process:

Did You Know?

You know that a landslide is quick downhill movement of loose rocks and soil. Similarly, a sudden slide of snow lying on loose snow from high mountains is called an avalanche. Like a landslide, an avalanche too can be triggered by earthquakes.

The worst avalanche occurred in Peru in 1970, triggered by an earthquake. It killed over 20,000 people.

prepaze

DIY Volcano

Let's make a volcano. Take the help of an adult to procure the materials required.

What you need:

- 2 tbsp of liquid soap
- 2 cups of cold water
- 4 cups of white vinegar
- Orange food color
- Half a cup of baking soda
- An empty 1.5 litre soda bottle

- 2 buckets of soil
- A beaker or a mug
- A spoon
- Old newspapers
- Safety goggles
- An apron

What to do:

Note: Do this activity in an open space. Put on your safety goggles and apron.

 Layout the old newspapers on the floor.

 Heap the 2 buckets of soil onto the paper.
Make a hole in the sand at the center and insert the empty soda bottle.

 Build a sand mountain around the bottle. Use some water to firm the soil, if required.

 Pour 2 tablespoons of the liquid soap, half cup of vinegar, and a few drops of the orange food coloring into the bottle.

 Now, add about 3 spoons of the baking soda into the bottle and step away.

 Repeat the activity by varying the amount of vinegar and baking soda. Record your observations.

What did you observe?	Why do you think that happened?

Research on the web and write what happened inside the volcano. Why and how did your volcano erupt?

_____

_____

_____

_____

_____

_____

_____

_____

prepaze

Make a Poster

Design a poster for alerting your neighbours about a possible flood in your area. Make it colorful and attractive.

prepaze

DIY Fossil

Let's make a fossil 'look alike.'

What you need:

➤ Cardboard

➤ Tissue papers

➤ Water

➤ Jute rope or half centimeter thick rope

➤ Pencil

➤ Glue

➤ Water colors

➤ Color pencils

➤ Fine sand

What to do:

Step 1 Take the cardboard and trace any sea animal of your choice. You could also pick one from the images below. Try to draw them life-size.

Step 2 Apply glue on the lines of your drawing.

Step 3 Stick the jute rope along the lines of the image. Also stick ropes in places where there could be prominent bones in the organism.

Step 4 Let it dry for 30 mins..

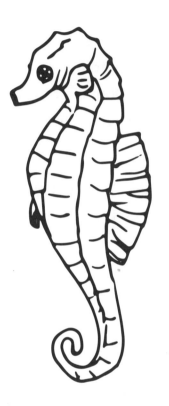

 Separate out tissue papers into single sheets.

 Apply glue generously on the cardboard and over the rope too.

 Stick the separated tissues on the cardboard, like making a collage. Ensure that the surface is not smooth. Apply pressure on the areas where you have pasted the ropes.

 Leave it to dry. You will observe the outlines of the animals where the rope is stuck pops out.

 Repeat steps 6 and 7 and stick one more layer of tissues on the drawing.

 Color dark brown on the places that are raised on the cardboard and lighter shade of brown in the depressions.

 While the water coloring is still wet, take some fine sand in your hand and sprinkle them gently all over the painting.

 Let it dry for a couple of hours.

prepaze

The DIY sample

prepaze

Answers

English Answer Key

Complete Me!

1. that

2. whom

3. where

4. whose

5. who

6. which

Word Puzzle

```
        N X V                                                    L Y   U
      F I X B B F                                          O K L S H   E Z
    Q E Y O D J W Q B Y                                  X W G W Q F N A K H U K   G
      E I B [W H O] N W P W                              L C Z H F W R H B F O R N   G S H
    G V R N U M F B N H P R Y H P D                    M H K T H V V A E G A T H X R C S H D
    V R K I F U O K P Y R D Y C T              R       F K Y T K V J E L K Y       P M
      I R P L I Y J P Y [W] Z    [R E V E O] K Y F B K I E K H           A S
        S R P C Y M M E [H W] R K T E O A Y F R M J K F Y           E
          U A P K P [E] N D F K U X N F           B
                  K P M [N] D R E O K A Y
            M X F W U [R]     [W H I C H] E B
          I V N C U D D [W] T Q O Z Y M       T
      U I I [R E V E H C I H W] P I T E E E T   E
    F X H H L A T B H O M N N I C D J Q P N T L Q S   P
    A L X H S T P O Q M E Y P Y F R A Y N F G X S Z   H S
  O P D D [Y H W] U A M H A C G Q H E Y T K N F N K Z X X   X
  P   C V P G Y H N A   G L B K Q J Y C F H S Q M L   X Q B
  V S   P V V X L U T   D C L Q O L Y V H Y X C E T K   S
  Q   T K S V Y Z J     C B P L N K Y F H E V Z B K K
    K Y T O Z           L D L Z S E Z Q
        D G R           D H S Z S J
                        S Z Q
                        Z
```

Change the Tense

1. I was walking in the park

Explanation: "Was walking" is the past progressive verb.

2. They were helping others.

Explanation: "Were helping" is the past progressive verb.

3. Where were you going?

Explanation: "Were going" is the past progressive verb.

4. They were studying.

Explanation: "Were studying" is the past progressive verb.

5. He was looking at the photos.

Explanation: "Was looking" is the past progressive verb.

6. She was painting.

Explanation: "Was painting" is the past progressive verb.

7. Jack was being nice.

Explanation: "Was being" is the past progressive verb.

8. I was reading.

Explanation: "Was reading" is the past progressive verb.

 Which one Is It?

1. Present progressive

Explanation: "Is working" indicates an action progressive in the present.

2. Past progressive

Explanation: "Was chasing" indicates an action progressive in the past.

3. Present progressive

Explanation: "Are swimming" indicates an action progressive in the present.

4. Future progressive

Explanation: "Will be visiting" indicates an action progressive in the future.

5. Present progressive

Explanation: "Is raining" indicates an action progressive in the present.

6. Future progressive

Explanation: "Will be closing" indicates an action progressive in the future.

Crossword Puzzle

Across/Down grid:
- 1. m a y
- 1 down: u s t
- 2. w
- 3. m i g h t
- i l
- 4. c o u l d
- a
- 5. n e e d

Missing Verbs

1. May

Explanation: The verb "may" is used when seeking permission.

2. need

Explanation: "need to be done" completes the sentence. "must" cannot be added before "to."

3. Would

Explanation: "would" indicates possibility of someone minding your presence.

4. must

Explanation: "must" indicates strong necessity of staying home.

5. will

Explanation: "will" indicates commitment.

order of Adjectives

Jumbled Sentences

1. We bought a new blue van.

Explanation: order is - determiner (a), age (new), color (blue), noun.

2. I see a big red plastic box.

Explanation: order is - determiner, size, color, material, noun.

3. Mom uses an old Italian pasta recipe.

Explanation: order is - determiner, age, origin, noun.

4. She gave a cute little round bowl.

Explanation: order is - determiner, opinion, size, shape, noun.

5. It is a beautiful black metal lamp.

Explanation: order is - determiner, opinion, color, material, noun.

Answers may vary.

Prepositional Phrases

Complete Me!

1. outside   4. into

2. over   5. on

3. from

Make Sentences

Answers may vary.

Fragments and Run-ons

Match the Parts

She is - looking out the window

They are - gathered to welcome him

Bikes of all kinds - are in the shop

After I leave home - I'll call you

He wrote - to explain why she did that

Fragments, Run-ons, or No Error?

1. fragment   4. fragment

2. no error   5. run-on

3. run-on   6. fragment

Answers may vary.

1. A project that was difficult to make.

Explanation: The teacher assigned me a project that was difficult to make.

2. When you are on the road.

Explanation: When you are on the road, you should be careful.

3. Make up a story.

Explanation: People make up a story when they are caught.

4. With the holidays around the corner.

Explanation: We can't waste any more time with the holidays around the corner

5. Trying to convince me.

Explanation: He's trying to convince me.

1. It is sunny today, so we are going to the beach.

Explanation: The two independent clauses can be connected by a comma and a coordinating conjunction.

2. You can meet the warden; she will show you the room.

Explanation: Two independent clauses can be joined by adding a comma and conjunction or by adding a semicolon.

3. It started to rain, yet we continued playing outside.

Explanation: Two independent clauses can be joined by adding a comma and conjunction or by adding a semicolon.

4. We usually read before bed; sometimes our mom reads to us.

Explanation: Two independent clauses can be joined by adding a comma and conjunction or by adding a semicolon.

5. It's gross. I don't want to see it ever again in my life.

Explanation: A period can be used to split the sentences.

 **This or That?**

1. dessert   5. loose   9. there

2. desert   6. lose   10. their

3. its   7. than   11. They're

4. It's   8. then

 **Make Sentences**

Answer may vary.

 **Capitalization**

 **Find Me!**

1. <u>my</u> favorite movie is <u>the lion king</u>.

Explanation: Need to capitalize the first word of the sentence and movie title.

2. <u>violet</u> and <u>i</u> are cousins.

Explanation: Need to capitalize the first word of the sentence, which is also a proper noun here. The pronoun I should always be in capital letters.

3. <u>next</u> week we have tests on math, <u>english</u>, and <u>spanish</u>.

Explanation: Need to capitalize the first word of the sentence, and names of languages.

4. <u>my</u> birthday is on 20th <u>july</u>.

Explanation: Need to capitalize the first word of the sentence and name of a month.

5. <u>we</u> visited the <u>statue</u> of <u>liberty</u> on the <u>thanksgiving day</u>.

Explanation: Need to capitalize the first word of the sentence, name of a monument, and name of a holiday.

fix Me!

1. He said, "I won!"

Explanation: Direct speech should be written in quotation marks, and a comma goes before the quotation mark. The exclamation or period in the end should go within the quotation mark.

2. Who did that?

Explanation: An interrogative sentence should end with a question mark.

3. They are good, funny, and hardworking.

Explanation: A series of words is used to describe. Commas are used between items in a series.

4. Oh dear! She must be devastated.

Explanation: "Oh dear" is an interjection - an exclamation mark is needed. The sentence can end with a period or another exclamation mark.

5. She went to California last week; she will return this weekend.

Explanation: This sentence is a run-on. A semicolon can fix it.

Spelling

Unscramble the words

1. HUNGRY

2. SWITCH

3. APRIL

4. SPACE

5. GRADE

6. DISCUSS

7. MYTH

8. SOUND

Spot the odd one

1. plaine

Explanation: The correct spelling is: plain

2. teamate

Explanation: The correct spelling is: teammate

3. hyperbol

Explanation: The correct spelling is: hyperbole

4. whistel

Explanation: The correct spelling is: whistle

5. athelete

Explanation: The correct spelling is: athlete

6. grammer

Explanation: The correct spelling is: grammar

Multiple Meaning Words

Show the Difference!

Answer may vary.

Crossword Puzzle

ACROSS: 2. pool; 4. kind; 5. foot

DOWN: 1. pounds; 3. light

Context Clues

Guess the Meaning!

1. talkative

Explanation: The clue words are: kept talking

2. agreed

Explanation: The clue words are: able to bring & request

3. silly or unimportant

Explanation: The clue words are: not taken seriously

4. changing

Explanation: The clue words are: difference performance every time

5. unsuccessful

Explanation: The clue words are: taken away

6. different

Explanation: The clue words are: successful and creative, which indicate she was different and more than regular.

Give a Context

Answer may vary.

Pair It Up!

1. overcook
2. amoral
3. disapprove
4. encase
5. megaphone
6. submarine

1. kindness
2. clockwise
3. humorous
4. seasonal
5. movement
6. wonderful

Prefixes and Suffixes

This or That?

prefix: invisible, react, enjoy

suffix: quietly, beautiful, neighborhood

no affixes: fun, school, struggle, week, company, class

Reference Materials

Word Chain

Answer may vary.

Figurative Language

Simile or Metaphor?

1. Simile: The morning weather is directly compared to ice.

2. Metaphor: A smile cannot light up a room, but a smile is compared to the effect similar to that of a light.

3. Simile: The speaker compares his or her hunger directly to the hunger of a bear.

4. Simile: Sleep is directly compared to a log.

5. Metaphor: He is not an owl, but his nocturnal nature is compared to that of an owl.

Answer may vary.

Answer may vary.

Antonyms

What Is My opposite?

1. separately   4. bored

2. unfriendly   5. left

3. left   6. gentle

Answer will vary.

1. length X width/breadth

2. neat X untidy

3. under X above/on

4. cheap X expensive/costly

5. borrow X lend/give

6. shallow X deep

7. weak X strong

8. cruel X kind

Riddle

Answer: bookkeeper.

Pandora's Box

Story Elements

1. May, John, and Lance
Explanation: The opening sentence lists her friends' names.
2. to dig up the worm Becka was talking about
Explanation: The friends decide to go to the yard

after Becka mentioned the worm.
3. It means a mysterious box that leads to disaster when opened.
Explanation: May called the eerie looking box as Pandora's box, but when

frightening things happen after opening the box, May confirms that it is very similar to the mythological Pandora's box.
4. in the tree house
Explanation: They hid the chest in the tree house.

order Me

1. Becka saw a huge worm in her yard

2. Friends geared up to find the worm

3. Dug up the yard

4. Found a treasure chest instead of the worm

5. Hid the treasure chest

6. Friends were in trouble

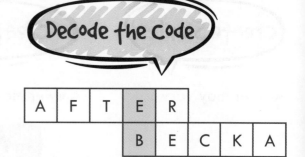

Decode the Code

A	F	T	E	R

	B	E	C	K	A

P	A	N	D	O	R	A

		H	O	U	S	E

	D	I	G

		O	T	H	E	R

B	E		G	O	O	D

Bullying

Story Analysis

Answer may vary.

1. She was quiet as she did not know anyone in the new school.

2. It is hard for some people to make friends. She was nervous and withdrawn as others were mean to her.

3. Some children like drawing attention to themselves. They create a scene and hurt others.

4. The narrator felt left out at her brother's party and that made her relate to Penny's situation in classroom.

Connecting to Text

1. Answer may vary.

2. Answer may vary: social bullying - where someone is alienated. Cyber bullying - is done using electronic means such as mobile phones or social media.

3. Answer may vary: I will try to help him/her.

4. Answer may vary: Tell them politely there's no fun in hurting someone else.

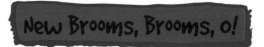

New Brooms, Brooms, o!

Poem Appreciation

1. third person

Explanation: The author refers to the characters with names and used the pronoun "he." Hence, the poem is in third person point of view.

2. forest

Explanation: Though wood can mean timber and substance, in this context it has to be forest as the father and son are said to live in the woods.

3. because his son was lazy and not helpful

Explanation: The first stanza clearly states that the father may not be happy with his son lazying around and not following his trade.

4. Answer may vary.

5. **Explanation:** Jack is portrayed as lazy and careless. He overslept because he does not care to help out his father. His father was annoyed seeing his son's behavior.

6. Cause: Jack sleeping all day. Effect: made his father shout at him.

Word Building

1. son - sun
2. there - their
3. one - won
4. where - were
5. maid - made

Make It Rhyme!

1. noon - soon
2. old - fold
3. broom - vroom
4. stump - grump
5. bill - still

6. trade - grade
7. sore - bore
8. passion - mention
9. work - perk
10. green - screen

Let's Rap?

Answer may vary.

Cinderella – A Fairy Tale

Read and Answer

1. good wins over evil

Explanation: The story is about Cinderella who represents goodness and kindness rising above the stepsisters and stepmother who represent evil.

2. stepmother and stepsisters

Explanation: They are the antagonists as they constantly make Cinderella's life miserable and don't even allow her to go to the ball or see the prince.

3. to take Cinderella to the ball

Explanation: A carriage is a vehicle.

4. the objects created by fairy's magic will return to normal

Explanation: The fairy warns Cinderella that the magic will fade away by midnight.

Story in Pictures

Answers may vary.

My Baby Sister

Story Analysis

1. Nash, his father, mother, and sister Eva.

Explanation: The text says "parents." So it's clear that there are father, mother, and children.

2. They went to the park.

Explanation: The mom took them to the park.

3. They played on the see-saw.

Explanation: The first activity mentioned in the text is see-saw. So, it can be inferred that they did that as soon as they reached the park.

4. She scraped her knees by falling off a swing.

Explanation: Eva was hurt as she fell off the swing.

5. Mom noticed when Eva cried.

Explanation: The mom came over after the accident.

6. Nash

Explanation: The narrator introduced himself in the beginning and has used the pronoun "I" throughout.

7. first person

Explanation: When the story is told from the speaker's point of view using the pronoun "I," it is first person.

8. Answer may vary.

Cause: Eva got excited. **Result:** asked Nash to swing higher. **Cause:** Eva fell from the swing. **Result:** hurt her knee.

Character Analysis

1. honest and caring

Answer may vary: He does not lose sight of his sister and is honest when confronted by his mom.

2. understanding and loving

Answer may vary: She noticed as soon as her child was hurt, and she understood it was an accident and Nash did all that he could.

order Me!

1. reached the park
2. played on the slide
3. fell off the swing
4. scraped the knee
5. went home

prepaze

Poem vs. Prose

1. poem: it's a poem because it flows with rhyming words, there is no specific plotline, or dialogs.

2. story/prose: it's a story because it has characters, settings, plotline, dialogs, etc.

3. a) A poem has figurative language, whereas a prose may not.

b) A poem does not follow any strict rules in terms of sentence structure, punctuation, or grammar, whereas a prose strictly follows the rules.

4. a) story - nory

b) another - brother

5. dad and grandma

6. a house

7. Answer may vary.

True or False or Not Given?

1. False   4. Not given

2. False   5. False

3. True   6. Not given

Elements of Poetry and Prose

Poetry: rhyme, figurative language, rhythm, stanza

Prose: grammar/punctuation rules, plot, characters, settings, dialogs, paragraphs

The Wind and the Sun

Read and Answer

1. Wind

Explanation: The arrogant remark indicates that Wind won the previous bet.

2. author

Explanation: The story is in the third person point of you as the writer is not a part of the story.

3. When wind blows, people brace themselves to feel warm and to keep their things from flying away.

4. Answer may vary.

Is It the Same?

1. b   3. b

2. a   4. b

Understanding the Text

1. We eat to get energy and nutrition.

Explanation: The answer is explicitly stated in the first paragraph.

2. They are juicy, tasty, and healthy.

Explanation: The answer is explicitly stated in the first paragraph.

3. Plants get energy from sunlight. Car gets energy from fuel. Phone and charger.

Explanation: The answer is explicitly spread across the last two paragraphs.

4. Phone's battery alert and car's fuel gauge can indicate they are used up.

Explanation: The children answer by relating to real life situation.

Make a List

Children: school, learn, play, exercise, fold clothes, tidy their rooms.

Adults: job, clean, cook, teach, exercise.

Answer may vary.

Find the Match

1. plants and animals need food - to grow

2. machine runs out of fuel - needs to be refilled

3. mobile phone is used - battery gets drained

4. body consumes the energy - brain receives the signal

Food for Thought!

Answer may vary.

Work as a Detective

1. <u>Plants get</u> energy <u>from sunlight</u>, and that energy is transferred <u>to us when we eat</u> the plants.

Explanation: The words "get from sunlight" and "to us" show movement.

2. Adults go to work, teach their children, exercise, and do many household chores <u>such as cooking, cleaning, and washing</u>.

Explanation: The word chores is followed by examples of chores to clarify its meaning.

3. Our stomach signals the brain that the energy is consumed and we need more energy. This cycle of taking in energy and <u>using it up</u> goes on and on.

Explanation: The meaning of consume is given in the following sentence.

Data Analysis

1. 60%
2. children who drop out and perform poorly academically
3. 10%
4. 50%
5. Answer may vary: Children don't report being victims as they may feel embarrassed or afraid.

Interpret Data

Transfer Data

Categories	Percentage
Drop out	20%
Experience bullying	60%
Fear school	10%
Perform poorly academically	20%
Don't report bullying	50%

Riddle

Answer: RHYTHMS

Math Answer Key

Froggy Loves Numbers!

a. 10, 15, 20, 25, 30, 35, 40, 45 (Any 8 numbers from the list)

b. 1, 2, 3, 4, 6, 9, 12, 13, 36 (Any 8 numbers from the list)

c. 1, 2, 11, 22

Say 'Yes' or 'No'!

a. Yes

b. No

c. Yes

d. No

e. Yes

Can You Number the Rail cars?

a. 8, 10, 12, 14 - Multiples of 2 in sequence.

b. 36, 54, 72, 90 - Multiples of 18 in sequence

Are Both the Lists Same?

Multiples of 56 - 56, 112, 168, 224, 280, 336, 392 (Students can list the first 5 multiples).

Factors of 56 - 1, 2, 4, 7, 8, 14, 28, 56.

No, the two lists are not the same.

Prime and Composite Numbers

Calendar Problem

Composite numbers: 4, 6, 8, 9, 10, 12, 14, 15, 16, 18, 20, 21, 22, 24, 25, 26, 27, 28, 30

a. Prime numbers: 2, 3, 5, 7, 11, 13, 17, 19, 23, 29, 31

b. Remaining: 1, 1 is neither a composite nor prime number.

Prime or Composite?

a. 4 shirts - Composite

b. 20 caps - Composite

c. 13 shoes - Prime

d. 39 bows - Prime

Expression	Answer	Prime or Composite	Factors
a. 8 x 6	48	Composite	1,2, 3, 4, 6, 8, 12, 16, 24, 48
b. 125 ÷ 5	25	Composite	1, 5, 25
c. 44 ÷ 4	11	Prime	1, 11
d. 20 + 15 +6 +2	43	Prime	1, 43
e. 12 x 4	48	Composite	1,2, 3, 4, 6, 8, 12, 16, 24, 48

a. Parker can buy a possible of 6 ice creams, since 30 is a multiple of 5.

b. Stella must have bought tickets for $2 or $4, since factors of 16 are 1, 2, 4, 8, 4, 16, and 3 is not a factor of 16.

c. George has 24 cars in all. 6 and 4 are factors of 24.

Color the Correct Puzzle

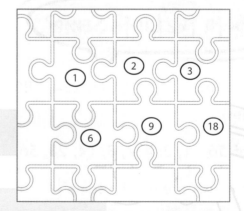

prepaze

Option A: 8

a. Option D: 8

b. Option B: 70

c. Option D: 2

a. 14

b. 1

c. Yes

d. 3

e. No, 2 is the only even prime number

f. No

a. 17, 19, 23, 29, 31, 37, 41, 43

b. 15, 16, 18, 20, 21, 22, 24, 25, 26, 27, 28, 30, 32, 33, 34, 35, 36, 38, 39, 40, 42, 44, 45

a. Factors of 60 = 1, 2, 3, 4, 5, 6, 10, 12, 15, 20, 30, 60

b. Any 4 multiplicative statements, a sample is given.

2 x 30 = 60

3 x 20 = 60

4 x 15 = 60

5 x 12 = 60

a. 2 x 12 = 24

b. 12 x 6 = 72

Factor Tree

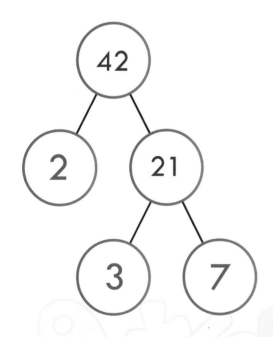

a. 42 = 2 x 3 x 7

b. We know that the factor tree cannot be branched further when the number in the branch is a prime number.

a. The sum of the digits is divisible by 3

b. The digit in the ones place is either 0 or 5

c. The digit in the ones place is either 0 or a multiple of 2

d. The digit in ones place will always be 0

e. The digit in ones place will always be an even number

a. 6, 9, 12, 18, 21, 24, 27, 30, 33

b. 1, 2, 3, 4, 5, 10, 15, 20

c. 7, 14, 21, 28, 42, 84.

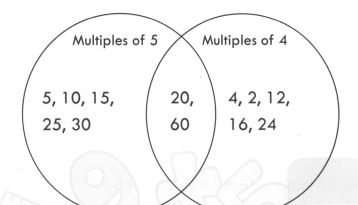

Classroom Problem

a. $48 \div 4 = 12$. 12 tables will be needed.

b. There can be groups of 2, 3, 4, 6, 8, 12, 16, 24, 48

c. No, because we will have 47 students and 47 is a prime number

Prime Factors

a. Factors of 12 = 1, 2, 3, 4, 6, 12

Factors of 18 = 1, 2, 3, 6, 9, 18

Common factors of 12 and 18 = 1, 2, 3, 6

The highest number that can divide both 12 and 18 is 6

b. 56, since 2 x 2 x 2 x 7 = 56.

c. False. It will only have 5 as its factor. For 2 to be a factor of a number, that number has to be even.

Comparison of Multi-digit Numbers

Miss. Liv's Math Lab

a. 9 x 4 is the same as 36

b. 36 is the same as 9 x 4

c. 36 is the same as 4 x 9

d. 36 is the same as 9 sets of 4

e. 36 is the same as 4 times 9

The correct options are:

a. 40 is 8 times as many as 5

c. 40 is 5 times as many as 8

d. 40 is the same as 8 sets of 5

George's Assignment

a. 9

b. 5

c. 4

d. 32

e. 24

f. 10

a. John has 28 marbles

b. Greg baked 18 cupcakes

c. A kangaroo can go 24 inches in one jump

d. Steve has 3 times more non-fiction books than fiction books

e. The skipping rope is 4 feet long

Solve the Expressions

Expression	Standard form	Word form
6 tens + 4 tens	100	One hundred
2 hundreds + 3 hundreds	500	Five hundred
6 thousands + 1 thousand	7000	Seven thousand
4 thousands + 11 hundreds	5100	Five thousand one hundred
5 hundreds + 7 tens	570	Five hundred seventy

Place Value Chart

a and b:

Ten Millions	Millions	Hundred Thousands	Ten Thousands	Thousands	Hundreds	Tens	Ones
		5	4	3	0	2	4

c. 543,024

d. Five hundred and forty-three thousand and twenty-four

a. Plane is faster than the bike by 20 miles

b. Brett sold 8 times more tickets than Ava

c. The tank holds 270 times more water than the jug

a. Set B has 4 times as many smileys more than set A.

b. 3 x 5 = 15

Who Has More Apples?

a. 5 + 4 = 9. Jack has 9 apples

b.   5 x 4 = 20. Steve has 20 apples

Solve the Word Problems

a. 3 cupcakes will be left out.

b. Joe is short by $2 dollars.

a. 15 - 5 = 10, Ken has to run 10 miles

b. 6 + 3 = 9, 9 + 15 = 24, 45 - 24 = 21, John has to save $21

c. 18 x 2 = 36, 14 x 3 = 4, 36 + 42 = 78; The girls made $78 in all

Two-Step Equations

a. Step 1: Set B = 8 x 4 = 32.

Step 2: After adding 5 more, Set B = 32 + 5 = 37.

Set B has 37 stars

b. Step 1: Number of marbles Adrian has = 9 x 5 = 45

Step 2: After giving 3 marbles to Ava, Adrian has 45 - 3 = 42 Adrian has 42 marbles

Joseph's Toy car

a. 7 represents the quotient, which means, Joseph, can buy 7 cars.

b. 2 represents the reminder, which means Joseph will be left with $2.

Adam Goes Shopping

Correct answers:

Adam bought 4 cartons each containing a dozen balls.

For 4 years, Adam bought 12 candles each year.

a. 3m + m = 20, 4m = 20, m = 5. Johnny has 5 markers and 15 pens.

b. 2s + s = 24, 3s = 24, s = 8. Johnny has 16 stamps and 8 stickers.

c. 4 x 4 = 16. Johnny has 16 pencils

a. $54 = 9 \times 6$

b. $21 = m - 5$, $21 + 5 = m$, $26 = m$

The value of m is 3 more than 23

a. $6 \times 8 = 48$, Ava bakes 48 cookies

b. $3 \times 48 = 144$, Ava's mom will bake 144 cookies

c. $48 \div 4 = 12$, Ava can make 12 packets

d. $5 \times 12 = 60$, Ava can make $60

Standard form	Expanded form	Word form
305,121	300000 + 5000+ 100+ 20 + 1	Three hundred five thousand one hundred twenty one
3, 505	3000 + 500 + 5	Three thousand five hundred five
2,589	2,000 + 500 + 80 + 9	Two thousand five hundred eighty nine
13,007	10, 000 + 3,000 + 7	Thirteen thousand seven
67, 280	60,000 + 7,000+ 200 + 80	Sixty seven thousand two hundred eighty

a. Number of markers with David = 2 x Number of markers with Stella = $2 \times 4 = 8$

David has 8 markers

b. Number of markers with Bob = 4 x Number of markers with David = $4 \times 8 = 32$

Bob has 32 markers

c. Number of markers with Zoe = 28

28 = number of markers with Stella x 4

Zoe has 7 times more markers than Stella

Movie Time!

3 x 3 = 9. The price of a ticket on Sunday = $9

a. 3 x 3.50 = 10.50. Yes, Sam can buy 3 tickets for Thursday

b. Sam needs $6 more

c. The ticket on Saturday costs twice as that on Tuesday

d. The ticket on Monday is two times less than the ticket on Friday

e. Sam has spent a total of $41

f. Sam will be left with $3

The price of one bouquet = $6

a. The least amount spent = $6. The most amount spent = $10

b. Each friend gets 3 vases

Patterns

What Next?

a.

b.

c.

d.

a.

b.

c. 4, 6, 5

d. 2, 3, 3

Missing Number!

a. 28 - multiples of 7

b. 28 - 8, 8+2, 10+4, 14+6, 20 +8

c. 1875 - multiply by 5

a. Brett places flowers in multiples of 2, so the sixth vase will have 12 flowers.

b. Nancy places the seed 3 times more than the previous packet., so in the next packet, there will be 81 seeds.

First Five

a. 3, 9, 15, 21, 27   b. 72, 63, 54, 45, 36   c. 2, 4, 16, 256, 65,536

Rules, Rules and More Rules

a. Add 12

b. The number is a multiple of 9

a. **12, 22, 32, 42, 52**

b. **14, 20, 26, 32, 38**

Rule	Pattern
a. Multiply 4	90, 85, 80, 75, 70
b. Add 11	1, 4, 16, 64, 256
c. Subtract 5	88,44, 22, 11
d. Divide by 2	1, 12, 23, 34, 45, 56
e. Add 7	7, 14, 21, 28, 35, 42

prepaze

a.

b.

c.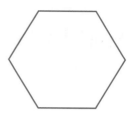

Complete the Pattern

a. 60, 66

b. 30, 25

c. 29, 25

Describe the Sequence

a. ABCC

b. AABB

Option b. 50, 74, 90

Monday - $4, Tuesday - $8, Wednesday - $12, Thursday - $16, Friday - $20, Saturday - $24, Sunday - $28.

a. Wednesday

b. Two days

c. $28

World of Candies

m	j
1	3
2	4
11	13
18	20
23	25
54	56

a.

b.

c.

The Fruit Bowl Problem

a. Pear   b. 8   c. Mango

A Starry Night

a. 12 15   18   21
   24   27   30

b. Multiply by 3

Input-output

a. Rule:
   Add 2

b. Rule:
   Multiply by the
   same number

c. Rule:
   Multiply by 3

Input	Output
2	4
6	8
10	**12**
12	14
21	23

Input	Output
3	9
5	25
7	**49**
4	16
9	81

Input	Output
2	6
3	9
0	**0**
1	**3**
7	21

The Wind and the Sun

a. 54,372

Ten Thousands	Thousands	Hundreds	Tens	Units
5	4	3	7	2

Fifty-four thousand three hundred and seventy-two

$50{,}000 + 4000 + 300 + 70 + 2$

b. 154,372

Hundred thousands	Ten Thousands	Thousands	Hundreds	Tens	Units
1	5	4	3	7	2

One hundred and fifty-four thousand three hundred and seventy-two

$100{,}000 + 50{,}000 + 4{,}000 + 300 + 70 + 2$

prepaze

c. 20,903

Ten Thousands	Thousands	Hundreds	Tens	Units
2	0	9	0	3

Twenty thousand nine hundred and three $20,000 + 900 + 3$

d. 76,340

Ten Thousands	Thousands	Hundreds	Tens	Units
7	6	3	4	0

Seventy-six thousand three hundred and forty $70,000 + 6000 + 300 + 40$

e. 880,536

Hundred thousands	Ten Thousands	Thousands	Hundreds	Tens	Units
8	8	0	5	3	6

Eight hundred and eighty thousand five hundred and thirty-six

$800,000 + 80,000 + 500 + 30 + 6$

Match the following

665,879	Twenty-three thousand eight hundred twenty
134,980	Seventy-six thousand nine hundred
23,820	Six hundred sixty-five thousand eight hundred seventy-nine
407,191	One hundred thirty-four thousand nine hundred eighty
76,900	Four hundred seven thousand one hundred ninety-one

prepaze

Fill in the Blanks

a. 100	d. 60,000, 20	h. 70,000, 7000	a. <	c. =	e. >
b. 100,000, 70	e. 400	i. 20,000	b. >	d. >	
c. 5	f. 5000	j. 30,000			

Who Will Win the Game?

Ruth won the game as he has the highest points.

Less Than or Greater Than?

Answers may vary.

Label and Represent

a. 10 x 5 thousands = 50 thousands = 50,000

Ten Thousands	Thousands	Hundreds	Tens	Units
5	0	0	0	0

b. 10 x 1 thousands = 10 thousands = 10,000

Ten Thousands	Thousands	Hundreds	Tens	Units
1	0	0	0	0

c. 6 thousands ÷ 10 = 6000 ÷ 10 = 6 hundreds

Ten Thousands	Thousands	Hundreds	Tens	Units
		6	0	0

d. 3 hundreds ÷ 10 = 300 ÷ 10 = 3 tens

Ten Thousands	Thousands	Hundreds	Tens	Units
			3	0

Unit form	Standard form
400	10 x 40
9000	900 x 10
500	5 x 100
4000	40000 ÷ 10
20	2 x 10
550	55 x 10
3200	320 x 10
3,000,000	6500 x 10
4040	4040 ÷ 10
6009	60,090 ÷ 10

Who Is Right?

Jessi wrote the correct answer. The other student swapped the tens and hundreds place.

Rounding off

Number Line Rounding off

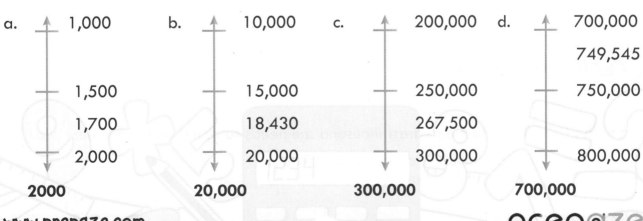

a.
1,000
1,500
1,700
2,000
2000

b.
10,000
15,000
18,430
20,000
20,000

c.
200,000
250,000
267,500
300,000
300,000

d.
700,000
749,545
750,000
800,000
700,000

Estimate

a. 842,150 = 840,000

222,802 = 220,000

Difference = 620,000

b. 842,150 = 800,000
222,802 = 200,000
Difference = 600,00

a. 357,908 = 360,000

148,567 = 150,000

Sum = 510,000

b. 357,908 = 400,000

148,567 = 100,000

Sum = 500,000

a. 30,000

b. 30,000

c. Because, 26,000 rounded up and 34,920 rounded down gives 30,000.

Burger Time

Nearest Thousand = 19,000

Nearest Ten thousand = 20,000

19,000 is more accurate than 20,000 as it is more closer to 18,550

a. i. Nearest Thousand: 500,000

ii. Nearest Ten Thousand: 500,000

iii. Nearest Hundred Thousand: 500,000

b. The answers are the same because in the thousands and ten thousands place 9 has been rounded off.

Maria Needs Help

To round off 328,702 to the nearest thousand she needs to round up the number 8 to 9. Thus, 328,702 should be rounded to 329000.

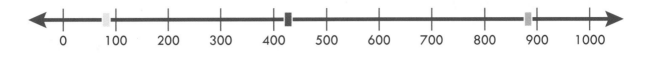

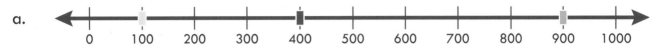

a.

70 rounded off to the nearest hundred is 100

438 rounded off to the nearest hundred is 400

b.

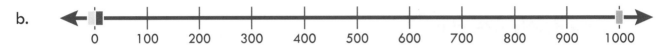

70 and 438 rounded to the nearest thousand is 0 as there is no thousandth value to round down.

Tens   30,000

Ten thousands   90

                8

a. 213,763 pebbles

b. 650,009 cars

c. 35,874 people

d. 24,145 liters of water

It is not different as the 6's in 6672 take the thousandth and the hundredth place and the 6's in 76672 take the thousandth and hundredth place as well.

a. Four hundred and fifty-six thousand three hundred and forty

b. One hundred and eighty thousand five hundred and thirty-six

c. Eleven thousand two hundred and thirty-eight

a. 3620 x 10 = 36,200, thus the cost of the bike is 36200 dollars.

b. Total toys = 45,000 + 900 = 54,000; 54,000 ÷ 10 = 54,000.

c. i. 2 million = 2,000,000

2 hundred thousand = 200,000

2,000,000 - 200,00 = 180,000;

City X has more population by 180,000

ii. City X has a population 10 times as many as City Y.

d. 850 x 10 = 8500;

Lisa's troop raised $8500.

prepaze

Possible numbers - 0,1,2,3,4

i. Number of men's shirts given away approximately=39,800 Number of women's shirts given away approximately = 26,900

The answers were found out by rounding off the numbers to the nearest 100's

ii. Total number of medals to be ordered approximately is 39,800 + 27,000 = 66,800

How Heavy Are the Gift Packages?

Weight of red package = 4,887 Weight of green package = 12,556

Thus, the total is 4,887 + 12,556 = 17,443 pounds

Weight of blue package = 2,677 Weight of green package = 12,556

Thus, the total is 2,677 + 12,556 = 15,233 pounds

Weight of blue package = 2,677 Weight of yellow package = 234

Thus, the total is 2,677+234 = 2,911 pounds

Thus, the combined weight is 20,354 pounds

A Tale of Two Friends

Debbie baked approximately 150 doughnuts

Elsa baked 44 + 149 = 193, approximately 200 doughnuts

a. Rounding off to nearest 10, 150 + 200 = 350; Debbie and Elsa baked approximately 350 doughnuts

b. 149 + 193 = 193; Debbie and Elsa baked exactly 342 doughnuts

c. Answers may vary

No of tourists in the month of march = 68,025 No of tourists in the first week of march = 15,614

No of tourists in the rest of the month = 68,025 - 15,614 = 52,411

a. 9,812 - 2,501 = 7,311

b. 17,032 - 3,133 = 13,899

c. 9,072 - 2,561 = 6,511

7,525 - 2,278 = 5,247; Thus 5,247 has to be added.

No of adults living in the city = 620,211 No of males living in the city = 316,101

No of females living in the city = 620,211 - 316,101 = 340,110 Therefore, the number of female living in the city are 340,110

Distribute and Solve

30 x (20 + 2)
Using the distributive property we get,
(30 x 20) + (30 x 2) 600 + 60 = 660

To calculate the perimeter we must add all the sides of the shape. To calculate the area, multiply the side lengths.

Shape A: Perimeter = 898 sq. m
Area = 34,650 m

Shape B: Perimeter = 548 sq. m
Area = 9,933 m

25 x 30 = 750; Therefore, 750 apples can be packed in 25 boxes.

a. 288
b. 111
c. 191

Juicy and Yum Yum

481 ÷ 4 = 120.
Each store received 120 bottles and 1 bottle was left.

1725 ÷ 5 = 345 oranges in each crate.

2,132 ÷ 3 = 710 - Q and 2 - R.
The ones digit can be changed to either 0, 3, 6, or 9.

248 ÷ 7 = 35 - Q and 3 - R

956 ÷ 4 = 239.
(800 ÷ 4) + (120 ÷ 4) + (36 ÷ 4) =
200 + 30 + 9

Decimal Numbers

a. 5 cm 7 mm

b. 57 / 10

c. 5.7

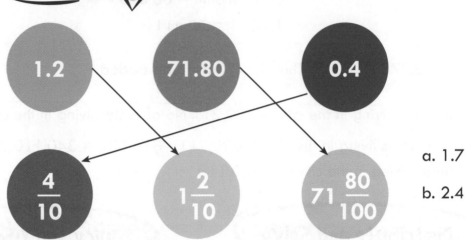

The Confused Clown

a. 1.7

b. 2.4

Will the fridge fit?

On comparing 67 inches and 72 inches, the fridge will fit.

Building a Math circuit

a. >   b. <   c. >

Fractions

a. $\dfrac{1}{5}$ or $\dfrac{3}{15}$ b. $\dfrac{6}{15}$ c. Example of equivalent fraction - $\dfrac{12}{30}$

b. $\dfrac{1}{2} = \dfrac{1 \times 4}{2 \times 4} = \dfrac{4}{8}$ c. $\dfrac{1}{2} = \dfrac{1 \times 2}{2 \times 4} = \dfrac{2}{4}$ d. $\dfrac{2}{3} = \dfrac{2 \times 2}{3 \times 2} = \dfrac{4}{6}$

$$\frac{4}{6}, \frac{1}{3}$$

$$\frac{2}{8}, \frac{3}{9}$$

$$\frac{1}{5}, \frac{5}{25}$$

$$\frac{2}{6}, \frac{6}{18}$$

$$\frac{1}{2} = \frac{3}{6}$$

a. Fraction for shaded part is $\dfrac{2}{3}$

b. Fraction for shaded part is $\dfrac{4}{6}$

c. Yes, a and b are equivalent fractions. $\dfrac{2}{3} = \dfrac{2 \times 2}{3 \times 2} = \dfrac{4}{6}$

a. <   d. >

b. >   e. >

c. <   f. <

b. >

$$\frac{4 \times 4}{5 \times 4} = \frac{16}{20} \qquad\qquad \frac{3 \times 5}{4 \times 5} = \frac{15}{20}$$

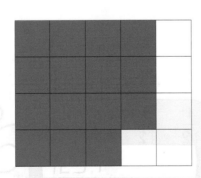

c. >

$$\frac{3 \times 6}{7 \times 6} = \frac{18}{42}$$

$$\frac{2 \times 7}{6 \times 7} = \frac{14}{42}$$

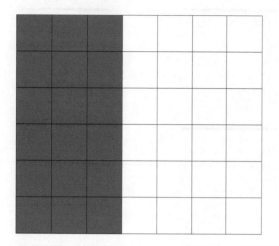

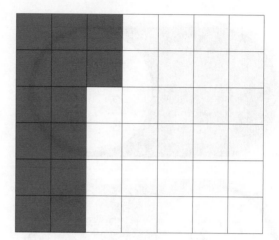

d. >

$$\frac{3 \times 7}{5 \times 7} = \frac{21}{35}$$

$$\frac{4 \times 5}{7 \times 5} = \frac{20}{35}$$

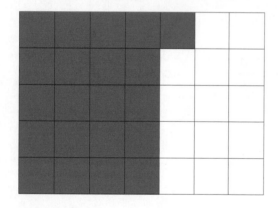

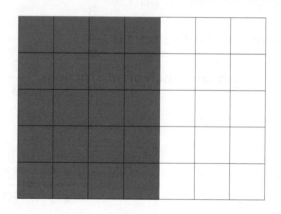

a.

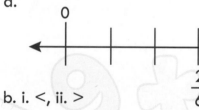

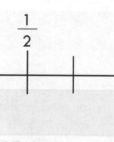

$$\frac{2}{6} = \frac{4}{12} \qquad \frac{5}{12} \qquad\qquad \frac{3}{4} = \frac{9}{12}$$

b. i. <, ii. >

c. Converted them to the same base and then plotted them.

Solve:

a. $\dfrac{3}{5}$ b. $\dfrac{3}{11}$ c. $\dfrac{2}{15}$ d. $\dfrac{2}{7}$ e. $\dfrac{8}{8} = 1$ f. $\dfrac{16}{19}$

b.

$$\dfrac{6}{19} + \dfrac{7}{19} = \dfrac{13}{19}$$

$$\dfrac{7}{19} + \dfrac{6}{19} = \dfrac{13}{19}$$

$$\dfrac{13}{19} - \dfrac{7}{11} = \dfrac{6}{19}$$

$$\dfrac{13}{19} - \dfrac{6}{19} = \dfrac{7}{19}$$

c.

$$\dfrac{6}{13} + \dfrac{5}{13} = \dfrac{11}{13}$$

$$\dfrac{5}{13} + \dfrac{6}{13} = \dfrac{11}{13}$$

$$\dfrac{11}{13} - \dfrac{5}{13} = \dfrac{6}{13}$$

$$\dfrac{11}{13} - \dfrac{6}{13} = \dfrac{5}{13}$$

d.

$$\dfrac{1}{9} + \dfrac{8}{9} = \dfrac{9}{9}$$

$$\dfrac{8}{9} + \dfrac{1}{9} = \dfrac{9}{9}$$

$$\dfrac{9}{9} - \dfrac{8}{9} = \dfrac{1}{9}$$

$$\dfrac{9}{9} - \dfrac{1}{9} = \dfrac{8}{9}$$

Decompose the Sum

b.

$$\dfrac{13}{11} = 1\dfrac{2}{11}$$

$$\dfrac{11}{11} \qquad \dfrac{2}{11}$$

c.

$$\dfrac{15}{13} = 1\dfrac{2}{13}$$

$$\dfrac{13}{13} \qquad \dfrac{2}{13}$$

d.

$$\dfrac{18}{9} = 2$$

$$\dfrac{9}{9} \qquad \dfrac{9}{9}$$

e.

$$\dfrac{18}{4} = 4\dfrac{2}{4} \text{ or } 4\dfrac{1}{2}$$

$$\dfrac{16}{4} \qquad \dfrac{2}{4}$$

f.

$$\dfrac{21}{5} = 4\dfrac{1}{5}$$

$$\dfrac{20}{5} \qquad \dfrac{1}{5}$$

prepaze

a.

$$\frac{8}{7} = 1\frac{1}{7}$$

$$\frac{7}{7} \quad \frac{1}{7}$$

b.

$$\frac{5}{3} = 1\frac{2}{3}$$

$$\frac{3}{3} \quad \frac{2}{3}$$

c.

$$\frac{10}{8} = 1\frac{2}{8}$$

$$\frac{8}{8} \quad \frac{2}{8}$$

d.

$$\frac{13}{6} = 2\frac{1}{6}$$

$$\frac{12}{6} \quad \frac{1}{6}$$

e.

$$\frac{11}{9} = 1\frac{2}{9}$$

$$\frac{9}{9} \quad \frac{2}{9}$$

f.

$$\frac{14}{5} = 2\frac{4}{5}$$

$$\frac{10}{5} \quad \frac{4}{5}$$

Find the Sum

b. $\dfrac{5}{10}$ c. $\dfrac{7}{12}$ d. $\dfrac{10}{9}$ e. $\dfrac{9}{8}$ f. $\dfrac{9}{12}$

Find The Difference.

b. $\dfrac{7}{10}$ c. $\dfrac{5}{12}$ d. $\dfrac{5}{9}$ e. $\dfrac{20}{14}$ f. $\dfrac{3}{12}$

Number Line Addition

b. $\dfrac{11}{8}$ c. $\dfrac{11}{12}$ d. $\dfrac{10}{9}$ e. $\dfrac{11}{6}$ f. $\dfrac{14}{9}$

b. $\dfrac{5}{9} = \dfrac{1}{9} + \dfrac{1}{9} + \dfrac{1}{9} + \dfrac{1}{9} + \dfrac{1}{9}$ c. $\dfrac{6}{7}$ d. $\dfrac{4}{5}$ e. $\dfrac{15}{6}$ f. $\dfrac{8}{3}$

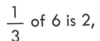

Oreo or Milo?

$\frac{1}{3}$ of 6 is 2,

Milo has 2 chew toys.

Olivia Likes Dancing

Week 1 - 5 x 1 = 5 hours

Week 2 - 4 x $\frac{3}{2}$ = 6 hours

Olivia spent more time in Week 2 and by 1 hour.

a. $\frac{2}{6}$ b. $\frac{3}{9}$ c. $\frac{4}{12}$

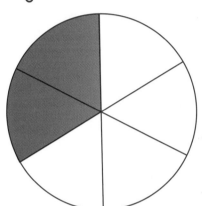
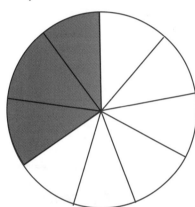
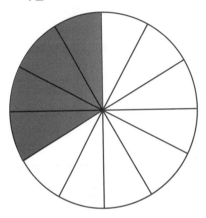

Answers may vary.

Measurement

Leon Goes to France

40 kg 516 g

Weigh Me Out

2 kg 121 g

1 kg 467 g

Pumpkin Pie

1 kg 225g

prepaze

Convert the Measurements

I.
a. 1000 g
b. 15000 g
c. 2450 f
d. 12 kg
e. 7125 g
f. 5 g
g. 4 kg 568 g
h. 25 kg
i. 5055 g
j. 5 kg 725 g

II.
a. 2000 m
b. 600 cm
c. 15 km
d. 11 m
e. 3210 m
f. 13 km
g. 414 cm
h. 8100 cm
i. 4980 m
j. 718 cm

III.
a. 1000 mL
b. 17000 mL
c. 3170 mL
d. 15 L
e. 6427 mL
f. 16 oz
g. 5 L 684 mL
h. 80 oz
i. 9065 mL
j. 7 L 552 mL

Johnson Builds a Wall

He worked 8 hours a day.

180 minutes

Grandma's Colorful Quilt

a. Area of red cloth = 24 sq. inch
b. Area of yellow cloth = 12 sq. inch
c. Area of green cloth = 21 sq. inch
d. Area of orange cloth = 8 sq. inch
e. Area of blue cloth = 16 sq. inch
f. Area of purple cloth = 20 sq. inch
g. Total area = 101 sq. inch
h. Cost of red, yellow and orange cloth together = $132
i. Cost of purple cloth = $4.10

$34.90

9 - 6 = 3. Steven can buy either 1 pencil - $2.75 or 1 eraser - $2.15 or 1 sharpener - $2.45

a.

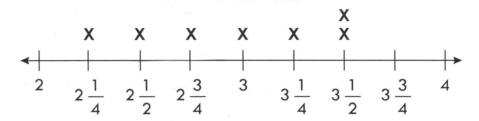

b. i. Matte   ii. Joseph   iii. 12 quarter inches   iv. ¼ or quarter inches   v. 10 inches

a.

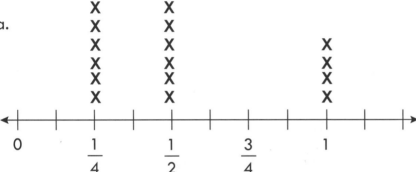

b. i. 10 jars

ii. 4 jars

iii. No jars

iv. She has the following jars,

- 4 One gallon = 4 gallons

- 6 Half gallons = 3 gallons

- 6 quarts = $1\frac{1}{2}$ gallons

4 gallons + 3 gallons + $1\frac{1}{2}$ gallons = 7 gallons.

Hence, all jars will hold only 7 gallons of liquid.

Line Plots

a. $7\frac{1}{4}$ feet

b. $3\frac{1}{4}$ miles

c. 3 inches

a.

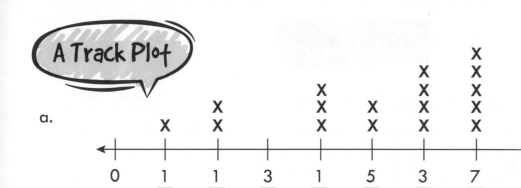

b. i. 2 students   ii. $3\frac{1}{8}$ iii. $\frac{6}{8}$ iv. 6/8 is equivalent to ¾, thus the total number of laps is 12/4 which is 3.

Weights of School Bags

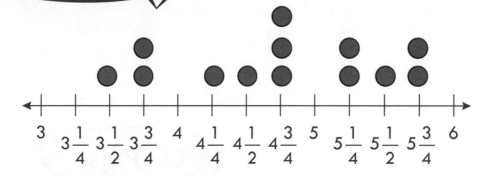

How Far Is Jennifer's Home?

a.

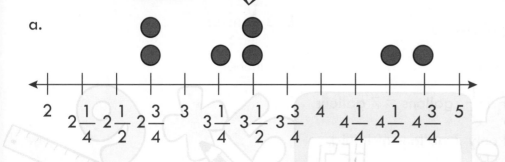

b. i. shopping mall B

ii. $\frac{1}{4}$ miles

iii. $4\frac{3}{4}$ miles

Geometric measurement

A House full of Angles

a. 135°

b. 90°

c. 180°

d. 8

e. 4

Estimate the Angle

a. 152°   a. 60°

b. 90°   b. 130°

c. 150°   c. 315°

d. 180°   d. 120°

Angle Mystery

Yes, the size of the circle does not yield different angle measurements.

Find the Angles

a. 280°   b. 180°   c. 360°   d. 30°

Draw Angles

a.

45°

b. 270°

c.

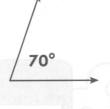
70°

d.

150°

prepaze

Clocks and Angles

a. Estimated angle 0°

b. Estimated angle 90°

c. Estimated angle 180°

d. Estimated angle 270°

Find A

a. $125 + 36 = 161°$

b. $98 - 64 = 34°$

c. $111 - 78 = 33°$

d. $46 + 44 = 90°$

e. $100 - 51 = 49°$

$<GEF = 16°$

Turn to the Right

Kristy - Fence   Hannah - Tree   Ron - Barn

Dr. Little's 180° Degree Turn

Towards his house.

How Many Quarter Turns Will Meredith Take?

4 quarter turns

Square and Hexagon Problem

18. $x = 150°$

14. $y° = 90° + 120°$ $z° = 60° + 30°$
$y° = 210°$ $z° = 90°$

Professions That Use Angles

Examples - Carpenters, architects, masons, artists, athletes

Geometry

Victor's Vacation

Mark the Arrow

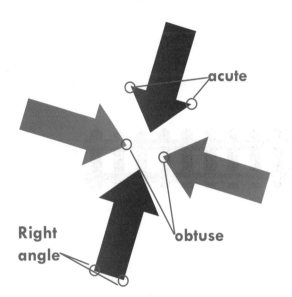

Do I Have Perpendicular Lines?

a.

b.

c.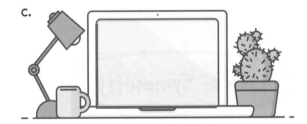

e. When the two lines intersect to form 90°, we know the lines are perpendicular.

d.

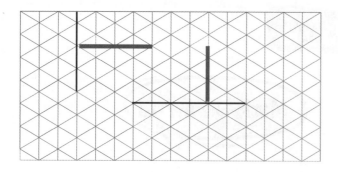

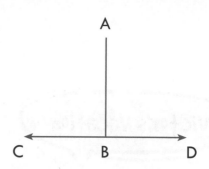

A

C   B   D

a. Parallel lines are marked in red.

b. Two lines are parallel if the distance between the two lines remains the same on every point of the line.

c.

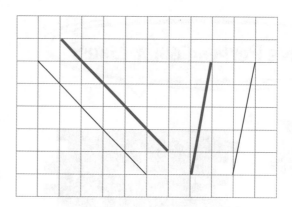

Line of Symmetry

a.

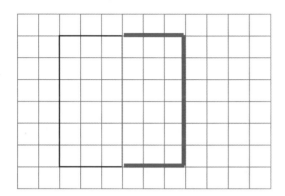

b.

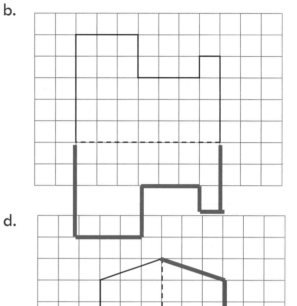

c.

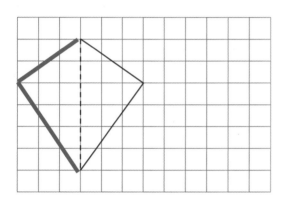

d.

At Which Turn Will
The cream fall off?

4 angles

Lines, Angles, and Symmetry

Answers may vary.

a.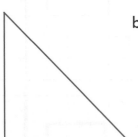

b.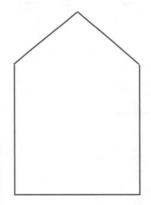

c.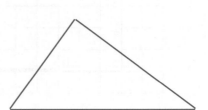

d.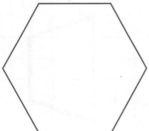

e.

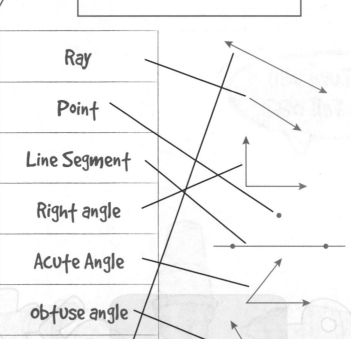

| Ray |
| Point |
| Line Segment |
| Right angle |
| Acute Angle |
| obtuse angle |
| Line |

prepaze

Science Answer Key

Word Grid

1. repel
2. series
3. transformer
4. fuse
5. parallel
6. conductor
7. insulator
8. attract
9. voltage
10. lightning
11. load

s	u	p	e	r	m	a	c	h	i	o	p	e	n	t	c
h	h	e	t	r	a	n	s	f	o	r	m	e	r	b	o
o	t	t	p	a	r	a	l	l	e	l	l	e	x	s	n
g	i	o	y	y	a	k	i	a	a	f	i	i	e	e	d
s	n	a	g	o	o	d	g	p	a	u	z	i	h	r	u
a	s	m	e	n	n	v	h	o	p	s	r	o	d	a	c
a	u	k	a	v	o	l	t	a	g	e	e	d	h	t	t
n	l	a	g	e	s	h	n	o	s	i	p	n	k	t	o
s	a	t	e	v	w	o	i	n	d	r	e	f	u	r	r
l	t	o	l	l	u	s	n	a	b	h	l	a	m	a	n
o	o	l	o	a	d	h	g	r	s	o	i	n	g	c	y
r	r	e	i	g	n	y	d	a	a	w	w	e	n	t	l

Race Your Can Without Touching It

1. The can moved away from the balloon.   moved away from

2. Repulsion   same

3. Negative charges   static electricity

prepaze

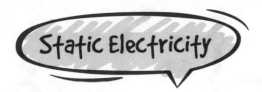

Static Electricity

1. Attract

Reason: One balloon carries positive charges and the other balloon carries negative charges. Opposite c harges attract.

2. Repel

Reason: Both the balloons have the same amount of negative charges. Same charges repel.

3. No movement

Reason: Both balloons have equal number of positive and negative charges on their surfaces. Hence they a re neutral.

Connecting Circuits

1. a. Series circuit

2. a. Yes

When Bulb C burns out, the electric current still can flow through in another path through Bulb B. Bulb B will still glow.

3. A switch

DIY Night Lamp

3. Circuit A, because it is a parallel circuit.

4. I will open the switch and stop the electrical current from flowing. Next, will remove one of the bulbs from its holder then close the switch. Only one bulb in my circuit will glow and it will be less brighter than two bulbs glowing.

Electrical Energy in other Useful Forms

a. Electrical energy is converted into useful forms such as heat, light and motion.

b. train   motion   burner   fan   toaster

How do Doorbells Work?

1. When the button is pushed on. On switching on the current flows through the coil making it an electromagnet. This magnet attracts the metallic hammer to hit the bell.

3. The magnetic effect of a magnet cannot be turned on or turned off as in an electromagnet. This will keep the metallic hammer attracted to the bell. The doorbell will not be useful.

2. No

Electromagnets in Phones, Electric Motor, and Generator

A. 4	B. 2	C. 2
2	4	3
5	1	1
3	5	4
1	3	

Plants

Photosynthesis Word Grid

1. chlorophyll
2. oxygen
3. stomata
4. photosynthesis
5. roots
6. leaves
7. sunlight

p	v	a	a	d	i	a	m	m	a	j	k	k	m
a	h	m	o	c	f	s	u	n	l	i	g	h	t
s	r	o	e	h	e	r	a	g	a	m	o	k	e
m	u	l	t	l	i	z	l	e	a	v	e	s	u
o	o	t	y	o	g	o	o	d	s	v	a	n	d
s	o	l	i	r	s	t	h	a	v	a	k	l	i
m	u	j	e	o	x	y	g	e	n	k	e	h	n
a	v	r	a	p	k	a	n	c	h	e	k	c	h
z	u	b	i	h	n	m	s	t	o	m	a	t	a
i	r	a	n	y	n	i	k	a	h	a	n	i	p
v	b	l	n	l	b	i	o	t	r	e	r	o	b
o	t	e	m	l	e	d	i	o	n	g	s	o	x
o	r	o	o	t	s	t	h	i	k	i	n	i	u
j	i	t	h	u	j	i	l	a	d	i	n	i	s

prepaze

Process of Photosynthesis

1. Sunlight

2. Carbon dioxide

3. Water

1. chlorophyll

2. Stomata

Oxygen

Food/sugar

1. Plant A. Plant A has sunlight which is important for photosynthesis.

3. Plant B makes its food during the day in the presence of sunlight. It stores its food and uses it during the absence of sunlight.

Food Chains Around You

1.

Producers	Consumers
Flowers/Nectar	Bees
Seeds	Birds
Greens	Ryan

Create a Food Chain

1. Grass - Cow - Boy drinking milk
Gras - Cow - Tiger
Carrots - Rabbit - Tiger

2. Different food chains link together to form a food web.

3. Yes

4.

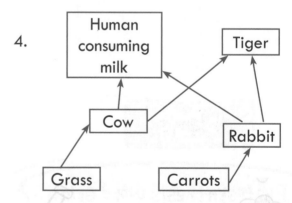

5. Herbivore: Cow, Rabbit
Carnivore: Tiger
Omnivore: Human

1. Five food chains

2. Food chain 1:

Marsh grass → Grasshopper → Shrew → Hawk

Food chain 2:

Marsh grass → Grasshopper → Shrew → Snake → Hawk

Food chain 3:

Cattail → cricket → frog → snake → hawk

Food chain 4:

Cattail → cricket → shrew → hawk

Food chain 5:

Cattail → cricket → shrew → snake → Hawk

3. a. Grasshoppers and crickets will be in excess.

b. Snakes and hawks will be left with less or no food if the food chain continues.

c. With no shrews in the food chain, very less number of crickets and grasshoppers will be eaten. Hence they will be in large numbers. The snakes which feed on shrews will be left with no food. They eventually will die out. Hawks that feed on snakes will in turn have no food to feed on. They too will eventually die out.

Food Webs around You

2. a. I will place the decomposers at the end of the food web because they feed on dead organisms.

b. Yes. Decomposers are consumers. They cannot make their own food and hence feed on dead plants and animals. Example; bacteria/mold/fungus/beetles/flies/earthworm

Ecosystem

Ecosystem and Its components

1. Living things
- Water birds
- Water plants
- Fishes
- Worms
- Insects
- Frog

Nonliving things
- Soil
- Water
- Sunlight
- Air

2. a. Plants - They will slowly die out due to lack of water.

Birds - They will lose food as the fishes would die. They will have no place to make their nests.

Worms - They will die because of lack of water and nourishment.

Fish - They will die due to lack of water and food (worms).

Frog - They will either slowly die out due to lack of insects or move to other areas in search of other food.

Insects - They will either die due to lack of food from plants or move to other areas in search of food.

b. If there is enough rain, the pond can go back to normal.

Desert Ecosystem

1. (Any three)
Some deserts are cold.
Some deserts are very hot.
Deserts are dry.
Deserts receive very less rainfall.
Many living things can be found in the desert.

2. (any three)
Long eyelashes to keep out sand in the desert.
Wooly fur on the legs and hump to keep warm during cold weathers. Long legs to keep camel off hot sand in the desert.
Padded/ broad feet to prevent the camel's feet sinking into the sand. Slit in the nostrils to keep out sand.

1. Rainforest ecosystem

2. c. Canopy

3. Snakes, tree frogs and toucans.

4. Air, rain (water), sunlight, soil

5. Without sunlight, the plants and trees will stop making food. Animals that obtain food from trees will be left without food.

Trees will die. Animals living in the trees will be left with no shelter. If there is no soil, trees cannot grow.

If there is no rain, plants and big trees might dry out.

(accept any of the above)

Interdependence of organisms

Interdependence between Plants and Animals

Plants and animals that are dependent on each other	How is the plant dependent on the animal?	How is the animal dependent on the plant?
Bee sitting on a flower	The pollen from the stamen will stick on the bee. When the bee sits on another flower, the pollen will drop off. (OR) The bee helps the flower in pollination.	The bee gets nectar from the plant to feed on.
Bird eating papaya fruit and seeds	The bird eats the fruit and seeds and leaves the seeds in the waste on soil. The seeds might grow into new plants.	The bird gets food (fruit) to eat. The bird also gets shelter on the tree where it can build nests.
Squirrel eating nut on a tree	The squirrel eats nuts and leaves waste on the soil. New plants can grow.	The tree provides shelter to the squirrel where it can live.

Changes in the Ecosystem

1. a. Cutting trees to construct buildings

   b. Add smoke and dirt to air / pollution

   c. Making water dirty which makes it harder for animals to live.

2. a. Storms/hurricanes

   b. Forest fire

   c. Climatic change

Adaptations in Animals

Mimicry

Camouflage

To survive dry conditions (or)

Storing water

Harmful and Useful Microorganisms

The mold in the stale bread causes disease in our body if we eat the stale bread. It is harmful. The bacteria in our stomach help in breaking down the food we eat. It is useful.

Rocks and Minerals

Properties of Rocks

Properties	Name of Rock	Type of Rock
Formed above the ground Very light in weight Feel crumbly, scratchy	Pumice	Igneous
Formed from bits of sand cemented together Sand is made of the mineral quartz May show ripples if it was formed under water	Sandstone	Sedimentary
Formed from granite Has layers across the rock Has minerals that are large enough to be seen	Gneiss	Metamorphic

Uses of Rocks

Properties	Uses of the rock	Name of the rock	Type of rock
Formed at the bottom of the oceans **Often has fossils** **Formed from bones and shells**	**Can be used to make chalk**	**Limestone**	Sedimentary
Formed from sandstone **Has small minerals inside** **Does not have layers**	Can be used for making glass and pottery	**Quartzite**	**Metamorphic**
Formed from shale **Has small mineral and feels smooth**	**Can be used to make roof tiles**	Slate	**Metamorphic**

Sedimentary and Metamorphic Rocks

A.	6	B.	5
	4		4
	5		2
	2		3
	1		1
	3		6

Minerals

Crossword on Minerals

Across

4. hardness
7. minerals
10. feldspar
12. calcite

Down

1. copper
2. aluminium
3. ores
5. streak

6. mica
8. luster
9. pyrite
11. diamond

prepaze

Identifying Minerals

1. John's rock has the mineral h ornblende.

2. Rio's rock has the mineral feldspar.

3. Hardness of John's rock can be 6.

4. I t is given that John's rock could scratch feldspar but not quartz. So, it could have the same h ardness as that of feldspar.

5. Yes

The hardness of hornblende is similar to that of feldspar. Minerals can scratch minerals that have t he same hardness or lesser hardness.

Processes that Change Landforms

Changes in Landforms

1. Physical weathering

2. Freezing and melting

3. Deposition

4. Chemical weathering

5. Delta

6. Horizons

7. Valley

8. Glacier

9. Canyon

10. Humus

1. Soil is formed when rocks are broken down into smaller and smaller pieces over time. They form layers over time called the horizon.

2.

This is horizon A. This is the topsoil. Plants and animals grown in the layer. This layer also has the humus on top. Humus is made of rotten dead plants and animals. There are very few rocks in this layer.

This is horizon B. It is called the subsoil. Broken pieces of rocks are scattered throughout this layer. Some plants grow deep roots into this layer.

This is horizon C. It has large chunks of broken rocks. There are no plant roots growing here. Below the broken chunks are large rocks that are yet to be broken. It is called the bedrock.

Preventive Measures of Soil Erosion

1. The strong winds and rains have caused soil erosion washing away the small plants.

2.

Things that George and Martha can do on the farm	Effects
They could plant trees on their farm. (OR) They could plant the coffee plants in strips - coffee plants and plants that hold soil.	Roots of the trees will hold soil that will slow down erosion. (OR) Other plants in between coffee plants will grow roots and hold soil.
They can plough their field across and not up and down.	This will prevent soil from running downhill if there are rains.

Slow and fast changes

	Name of the effect	Damages that occur	Two ways we can save ourselves from it
Effects of movement of plates on land	Earthquake	Ground shakes and splits open / cracks are formed. Tall buildings fall off. Sometimes mountains are formed. Can trigger landslides.	Move under a sturdy table to prevent things falling on your head. Move to open spaces where there are no buildings or power lines. (Accept any other relevant answer too)
Effects of movement of plates inside water (ocean)	Tsunami	Causes giant waves. They can wash away beaches, lives and property.	Listen to news warnings. Move to higher ground. Stay away from beaches. (Accept any other relevant answer too)

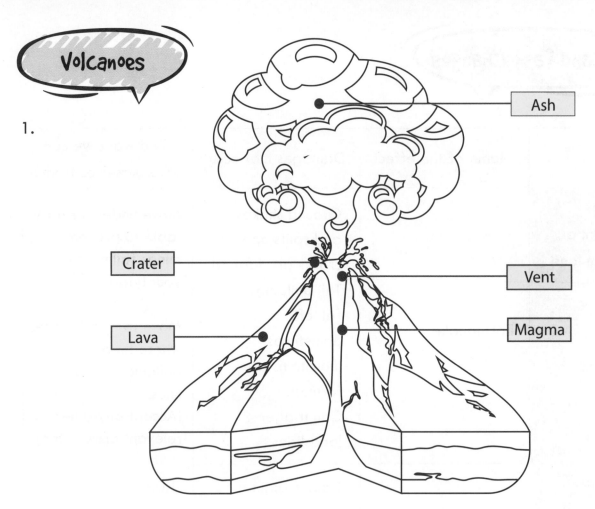

Volcanoes

1.

Ash

Crater

Vent

Lava

Magma

2. Igneous rocks can be found. These rocks are formed by cooled volcanic lava. Granite is an example of igneous rocks.

Processes that Change Landforms

- Physical weathering processes
- Chemical weathering processes
- Wind
- Moving water (such as rivers)
- Glacier movement
- Formation of sand dunes
- Formation of barriers

- Landslides
- Mudslides
- Floods
- Earthquakes
- Tsunami
- Volcanic eruptions

prepaze

www.aceacademicpublishing.com

THE ONE BIG BOOK

For English, Math, and Science

GRADE
4

 Ace Academic Publishing

ACHIEVING EXCELLENCE TOGETHER